ARISTOTLE, GALILEO, AND
THE TOWER OF PISA

ARISTOTLE, GALILEO, AND THE TOWER OF PISA

BY

LANE COOPER

Professor of the English Language and Literature
in Cornell University

ITHACA · NEW YORK
CORNELL UNIVERSITY PRESS
LONDON: HUMPHREY MILFORD
OXFORD UNIVERSITY PRESS
1935

PRINTED IN THE UNITED STATES OF AMERICA
THE GEORGE BANTA PUBLISHING COMPANY,
MENASHA, WISCONSIN

TO MY FRIEND

OTTO KINKELDEY

LIBRARIAN OF THE UNIVERSITY LIBRARY
AND PROFESSOR OF MUSICOLOGY
IN CORNELL UNIVERSITY

PREFACE

The reasons why a person with my sort of training should write this book are given in the body of it. For the control of matters there which lie outside my usual fields of study I am deeply obliged by help from several of my friends and colleagues, among them, and particularly, Floyd K. Richtmyer, Professor of Physics, who has been patient enough to read all the manuscript with critical attention. One way and another, I believe I have made effectual use of every one of his queries and comments, including those that touched upon the arrangement of certain of the earlier paragraphs. Helpful suggestions have come to me from other sources, too, and I hope the book is the better for my use of them. For any shortcomings that may remain no one is responsible but the author, who nevertheless is rejoiced to think that this work is the first book to be formally accepted by the Council of the Cornell University Press for publication.

LANE COOPER

ITHACA, May 15, 1934.

CONTENTS

ARISTOTLE, GALILEO, AND
THE TOWER OF PISA

BY

LANE COOPER

ARISTOTLE, GALILEO, AND
THE TOWER OF PISA

It is still a common belief in America that Galileo, having ascended the leaning tower at Pisa, by a single dramatic experiment refuted an assertion of Aristotle that had not been challenged since the days of ancient Greece, nor then. Thus in a text-book of 'science' for our intermediate grades, the children at school, it is said, find a picture in which a little dark Italian man observes from the height of a slightly oblique tower two balls of different size that are airily poised, as it were, on their way to the ground; together the unequal objects are supposed to be falling, together they must land below. I have at length got hold of some such picture; the Library of Congress found it for me on page 28 of a book by Francis J. Rowbotham called *Story-Lives of Great Scientists*, which appeared first in England and then in America about fifteen years ago. In this illustration, on the left, the apse of the cathedral is partly in view. Above, on the right, Galileo leans from the summit of the tower; two spheres, one far bulkier than a man, the other small, are beginning their descent; and at a safe distance a crowd of spectators below spreads out from the cathedral. The unique experiment is supposed to have been performed about the year 1590, and to mark a turning-point in the history of science. I wish to call in question the correctness of this picture, and shall ask the reader to suspend judgment concerning the story it is supposed to represent until he has some grasp on the substance of the following pages.

[13]

And first, whatever Galileo did, or failed to do, at Pisa, in all his extant writings he never once mentions the leaning tower, and never talks of experimenting from it. Next, let us remember this: half a century and more before we have conjoint mention of him and the leaning tower, Simon Stevin of Bruges, according to his own assertion, had let fall two balls of lead, one ten times the weight of the other, 'from a point about 30 feet high' to a plank below, and 'they landed so evenly that there seemed to be only one thump.'[1] In a book dated 1605, Stevin says that he had done this 'long ago' with his friend John Grotius; the two men were bent upon demonstrating by 'experience' a mistake of Aristotle in the *Physics* and *De Caelo*.

Then why not mention the speed of 'falling' bodies in our title? Because Aristotle in his writings on physics never once uses the Greek word for 'fall' in relation to speed. Indeed, when we run through his extant works, as I have done with the *Index Aristotelicus*, examining every reference Bonitz gives to 'fall,' and noting some instances that he missed, the rarity of both verb and noun (πίπτειν, πτῶσις) in the literal sense[2] is very striking. In metaphorical and derived senses

---

[1] The original passage will be given later, p. 77 (No. 19 in the excerpts appended at the close).

[2] I have examined all the passages recorded by Bonitz for πίπτειν, πτῶσις, ἐμπίπτειν, καταπίπτειν, in all cases and inflections. In *Meteorologica* 1.1.339ᵃ3 and 1.4.342ᵃ11, 14, shooting-stars and thunderbolts are said to 'fall'; in *De Plantis* 1.4.819ᵇ33 'the leaves of some plants fall' (*i.e.*, some plants shed their leaves); *ibid.* 2.3.824ᵇ8, the air will *descend* and bedew the ground; in *Historia Animalium* 3.3.514ᵃ7, if the veins in the neck are squeezed, the man falls in a faint; *ibid.* 8.5.594ᵇ12, a bear falls on its back to fight a bull; *ibid.* 8.12.597ᵇ9, quails 'fall' or descend; in *De Part. An.* 1.1.641ᵃ11 we have the 'fall' or stroke of a tool; *ibid.* 3.3.664ᵇ35, the tongue seldom 'falls' under the teeth—that is, seldom is caught between the teeth; in *De Somno* 3.4.457ᵇ4 the eyelids 'fall' or droop; in *Prob.* 26.3.940ᵇ15 the wind 'falls,' as also in 27.60.947ᵃ29;

Aristotle is much given to both forms, and to certain of their compounds; noun and verb are technically used by him, not at all as terms in physics, but in the realms of grammar, logic, and mathematics. So in *Metaphysics* 3.5.376^{b}19 we have 'the circle on which the lines from K fall.' In another field, his noun πτῶσις was taken over by the Latin grammarians as *casus* (*cf.* German *Fall*), which has become, in English, grammatical *case*. In *Physics* 7.2.343^{b}16 Aristotle uses the methodical term πίπτουσιν —'all fall under one or other of four heads'; *ibid.* 4.7.214^{a}23 gives us a sense, which, if technical, is not that of falling: 'The fact of motion in respect of place lends support both to those who hold that place is something over and above the bodies that *come to occupy* it [τὰ σώματα τὰ ἐμπίπτοντα], and to those who hold that the void is something.' But again in *Physics* 2.4.196^{b}9 this verb is used in a derived and methodical sense: 'How they fit into [ἐμπίπτουσιν] our division of causes.' There is a chance-reference to καταπίπτειν in *Physics* 2.6.197^{b}30-2 in illustration of the term 'automatic': 'A stone falls and hits some one, but it does not fall for the purpose of hitting him; it fell then "to no purpose"—for it might have fallen (the fall might have been caused) by some one, for the purpose of hitting the man.' Bonitz missed this quotation for the verb. If we may

---

ibid. 2.4.883^{a}37-8, the relation between the movement of the legs and the descent of the trunk is in question. In *Politics* 6.8.1321^{b}20 'falling houses' means falling into disrepair (similarly 1322^{b}21). To return to the *Meteorologica*, in 2.4.360^{a}33 'a great quantity of air might be moved by the fall of some large object without flowing from any source or spring'; *ibid.* 2.6.365^{a}5, tornadoes are produced when some winds are blowing and others fall on (rush against) them; *ibid.* 2.7.365^{a}20 we have Anaxagoras' naïve explanation of earthquakes as caused by ether caught (ἐμπίπτοντα) in hollows of the earth. In *Poetics* 9.1452^{a}9 the statue of Mitys falls upon his murderer who came to view it.

trust him, in the *Physics* there is no other occurrence of either verb or noun, and in *De Caelo* 'fall' simply does not occur.

I lay stress upon observation of the words Aristotle uses, since direct observation is a basis of scholarship and science; and, further, the story of the relations between Aristotle and Galileo seems to turn upon questions of observation as against opinion taken at second hand. Thus all the teachers of physics I have talked with seem to have observed the action of a light object, like a feather, and a heavy one, as a piece of lead, when dropped in a partial vacuum; all apparently have seen the laboratory experiment, and there have watched heavy and light objects behaving as Aristotle said they must behave in a vacuum—only that he did not believe a complete vacuum possible.[3] Whereas, of all the persons in my circle of acquaintance, I, a teacher of English, am the only one I can find who actually has gone, as Stevin says he and his friend did, to a sufficiently high point and dropped two stones, say, of different weights in order to watch how they would behave before and as they landed. From a good deal of inquiry I feel justified in saying that most teachers of physics at the present day believe what they believe about bodies falling through the air for some reason other than direct observation. Some believe it because they believe that Galileo went as high as he could in the leaning tower of Pisa, and dropped two objects of differing weights which hit the ground below together. But whether Galileo ever did that is still a question. Another of my friends in physical science believes that, of two weights released at the surface of the water, the heavier will reach bottom first. I tested his belief in private, and found

[3] *Physics* 4.8.216ª8-21; the passage is given below, No. 12; *cf.* p. 40.

it unsupported by the facts. Still another 'physicist,' the first one I asked about the downward motion of two unequal lead sinkers, was in doubt. Again, there are many who as aforesaid believe the story about Galileo and the tower of Pisa, and have no better ground for accepting the story than hearsay. They have read or vaguely heard that it was so; just as they believe that Aristotle said a certain thing about falling bodies of different weights, and that every one down to Galileo believed the same thing on the authority of Aristotle. As casual readers accept some modern authority for an opinion about the speed of bodies heavy and light in falling, so they accept upon authority, however vague, the tale about Galileo at Pisa. We may suspect that few 'scientists' have examined for themselves any evidence on the relations between Galileo and Aristotle; Galileo probably did better than most of his recent admirers in actually reading Aristotle, though on occasion he affects to quote from Aristotle words that are not found in Aristotle's writings.

We shall later examine the tale as it first appeared in Viviani's life of Galileo. This earliest biography of Galileo must have been written more than twelve years after his death, and well over sixty years after the assumed date (1590) of the episode at Pisa. Later, then, we can see whether the basic story has in it an element of myth. That in our day the tale has mythical traits is plain when we compare some recent variations in the telling. Whence, for example, come the dimensions of the objects Galileo is said to have let fall from the tower? Certainly not from Viviani, who does not even give a precise date for the occurrence. Galileo himself in his early work *De Motu* ironically asks what would happen according to Aristotle's theory if two balls of lead, one a hundred times heavier than the other, were let fall from the moon to the earth;[4] this passage did not see the light in Galileo's time, nor indeed till our own era, but was echoed by a passage in his *Dialogues concerning Two New Sciences,* which appeared in 1638, a passage very significant for the development of our myth, and one to which we shall recur.[5] In it we find, not Galileo, but 'Salviati,' a speaker in dialogue, attributing to Aristotle a statement which Aristotle never made: 'Aristotle says that "an iron ball of one hundred pounds, falling from a height of one hundred cubits, reaches the ground before a one-pound ball has fallen a single cubit." I [Salviati] say that they arrive at the same time.' Thus the question in the long unpublished treatise *De Motu* could be the ultimate source of the mythical weights which are cheerfully specified by R. A. Gregory in a book with the fine-sounding title, *Discovery, or the Spirit and Service of Science* (London, 1917, p. 2):

Members of the University of Pisa, and other onlookers, are assembled in the space at the foot of the wonderful leaning tower of white marble in that city one morning in the year 1591. A young professor climbs the spiral staircase until he reaches the gallery surmounting the seventh tier of arches. The people below watch him as he balances two balls on the edge of the gallery, one weighing a hundred times more than the other. The balls are released at the same instant, and are seen to keep together as they fall through the air until they are heard to strike the ground at the same moment. Nature has spoken with no uncertain sound, and has given an immediate answer to a question debated for two thousand years.[6]

[4] See below, pp. 81, 83.
[5] See below, pp. 90, 91, 92.
[6] Two thousand years would take us from 1591 to the year 408 B.C.; Aristotle died in 322 B.C.

Not very different is the account by Rowbotham which accompanies the illustration we have mentioned above, though the larger iron ball of the picture is so huge that no one man could ever carry it to the summit of the tower; it must weigh, not a mere hundred pounds, but several times as much as the little dark man who watches it descending, and the smaller ball is perhaps two-thirds the size of his head:

Galileo's first trial of strength with the university professors was connected with his researches into the laws of motion as illustrated by falling bodies. It was an accepted axiom of Aristotle that the speed of falling bodies was regulated by their respective weights: thus, a stone weighing two pounds would fall twice as quick as one weighing only a single pound, and so on. No one seems to have questioned the correctness of this rule, until Galileo gave it his denial. He declared that weight had nothing to do with the matter, and that it was the resistance of the air which determined the rate of speed of a body falling through it; if, therefore, two bodies of unequal weight could overcome the resistance to the same extent they would reach the ground at the same moment. As Galileo's statement was flouted by the body of professors, he determined to put it to a public test. So he invited the whole University to witness the experiment which he was about to perform from the leaning tower. On the morning of the day fixed, Galileo, in the presence of the assembled University and townsfolk, mounted to the top of the tower, carrying with him two balls, one weighing one hundred pounds and the other weighing one pound. Balancing the balls carefully on the edge of the parapet, he rolled them over together; they were seen to fall evenly, and the next instant, with a loud clang, they struck the ground together. The old tradition was false, and modern science, in the person of the young discoverer, had vindicated her position.[7]

[7] *Story-Lives of Great Scientists* [by Francis Jameson Rowbotham], pp. 27-9. The edition published in New York by the Frederick A. Stokes Company, of which the Library of Congress received a copy in 1919, was printed in England, being published [1918] by Wells Gardner, Darton, and Company. The English publishers more recently advertise the book as by F. J. Rowbotham

Whence, then, come the mythical ten-pound shot and one-pound shot of J. J. Fahie, a well-known English writer on Galileo? Apparently, for him and others these weights have crept into the story at second, third, or nth hand, from Stevin, who yet, as we saw, does not speak of cannon-balls. Let us not now go into disputable matters, such as the priority of Stevin, but take a few modern quotations as they come; first, Dampier-Whetham (1929):

> In 1591, Galileo, repeating an experiment of Stevinus, dropped a ten-pound weight and a one-pound weight together from the top of the leaning tower at Pisa, and showed the incredulous onlookers that, heavy or light, they struck the ground simultaneously.[8]

We turn to Fahie, doubtless the most reputable biographer of Galileo in England; he says (1903):

> Nearly two thousand years before, Aristotle had asserted that if two different weights of the same material were let fall from the same height, the heavier would reach the ground sooner than the lighter in the proportion of their weights.[9]

The foregoing quiet excerpt is here included so as to remind the reader that Aristotle nowhere makes precisely that assertion; the following, also from Fahie (1921), is given

---

and Ruth Cobb. With the picture we have noted in this book, compare the letter-head of The Principia Press of Bloomington, Indiana. Here we have the tower without Galileo, but with the balls or spheres, the smaller about even with the centre of the larger, so that the larger will reach the ground first! They are now about six-sevenths of the way down.

[8] *A History of Science and its Relations with Philosophy and Religion* by William Cecil Dampier Dampier-Whetham, Cambridge, 1929, p. 143. This author refers to Whewell, *History of the Inductive Sciences* 2.46; Whewell (*cf.* edition cited below 1.317 and passage No. 29) perhaps led him to think that Stevin describes his experiment in a publication of 1586. But an obliging correspondent, J. E. Kroon, in the Library of the University of Leyden assures me that the earliest description occurs in Stevin's *Opera Omnia* as published in 1605.

[9] J. J. Fahie, *Galileo, his Life and Work*, London, Murray, 1903, p. 24.

because the ultimate source of the statements in it, if they really had a proper source, could only be Viviani, yet details such as the ten-pound shot, and language such as 'blasphemy,' cannot be traced to the single passage of Viviani on which the whole story must depend. The excerpt therefore is mythical in a bad sense:

> Aristotle had said that, if two different weights of the same material were let fall from the same height, the two would reach the ground in a period of time inversely proportional to their weights. Galileo maintained that, save for an inconsiderable difference due to the disproportionate resistance of the air, they would fall in the same time. The Aristotelians ridiculed such 'blasphemy,' but Galileo determined to make his adversaries see the fact with their own eyes. One morning, before the assembled professors and students, he ascended the leaning tower, taking with him a 10 lb. shot and a 1 lb. shot. Balancing them on the overhanging edge, he let them go together. Together they fell, and together they struck the ground.[10]

Why 'one morning'? Viviani does not specify the year, let alone the time of day. Next we take a rather significant scholar, Wolfson, whose bias against Aristotle proceeds partly from the subject of his research, the Spanish Jew Crescas (1340-1410), but who may be forgiven his example from Galileo because of the present general belief in the story:

> Again, an experience to him [Crescas] was something given, not

[10] Fahie, *The Scientific Works of Galileo*, in *Studies in the History and Method of Science*, ed. by Charles Singer, 2 (1921). 216. The article on Galileo by Agnes Clerke in the last edition of the *Encyclopaedia Britannica* still retains the story as a fact, and assumes that Galileo was already quarreling with the 'Aristotelians'; there is no real evidence that he quarreled at Pisa. For another misleading account of the relations between Galileo and Aristotle, see Harlan T. Stetson, *Man and the Stars*, New York, 1930, pp. 47-9. See also *Galileo, Searcher of the Heavens*, by Émile Namer, translated and adapted from the French by Sibyl Harris, New York, 1931; pp. 28-31 contain the myth about the tower of Pisa, and in a rather elaborate version.

something that was to be produced. It never became with him an experiment. Crescas, for instance, doubted the truth of Aristotle's theory as to the existence of naturally light objects and of a natural motion upward, and thus when he observed that air goes down into a ditch without the application of any external force, he concluded that air was not naturally light and had no natural motion upward. But when Newton began to doubt these Aristotelian laws of motion, while he may not have received his original inspiration from the falling of the celebrated apple, he certainly did observe and study the falling of other bodies, and after long and painstaking research established the universal law of gravitation. Again, when Crescas wanted to prove that something was wrong with a certain conclusion which was supposed to follow from Aristotle's theory that heavier bodies fall faster than lighter bodies, he resorted to a hypothesis of an original time of motion. It was subtle, but it led nowhere. But when Galileo wanted to prove that Aristotle's theory was totally wrong, he climbed up to the top of the tower of Pisa, and let two unequal weights fall down at the same time, and watched their landing. It was simple, but it led to an epoch-making discovery in the history of science.[11]

Why 'epoch-making'? I have yet to learn what communal scientific advance arose out of Galileo's alleged experimentation from the tower of Pisa; there was no mention of it that can be traced before 1654; and if indeed the thing took place, it seems to have been overlooked by the world at large for sixty years and more. At Pisa itself, half a century after Galileo left his professorship there, queer notions about falling bodies could be entertained by one of his own

[11] *Crescas' Critique of Aristotle; Problems of Aristotle's Physics in Jewish and Arabic Philosophy;* by Harry Austryn Wolfson, Cambridge, Mass., 1929; pp. 126-7. I have not succeeded in consulting Julius Guttmann, *Chasdai Creskas als Kritiker der Aristotelischen Physik* in *Festschrift zum siebzigsten Geburtstage Jakob Guttmanns.*

followers, as we shall see from letters of Renieri, an able astronomer who also, in this later time, held the chair of mathematics. Meanwhile, for the earlier period, it is not unlikely that Stevin and Grotius did their experimenting before Galileo broke at all with the tradition of Aristotle; and, as we shall see, these two men of the North were by no means the first in Europe to attack Aristotle on the point they questioned. Let us turn, however, to other interesting variants with notable details that cannot be found in the basic account by Viviani. Here is the tale as delivered by H. Moore, 'B.Sc., A.R.C.Sc., F.Inst.P., Assistant-Director of Research, British Scientific Instrument Research Association, formerly Lecturer in Physics, University of London, King's College':

> In his experiments on the acceleration of freely falling bodies, Galileo enclosed equal weights of different materials in a number of exactly similar boxes. In this way the resistance offered to the passage of the boxes through the air was made the same in all cases for equal speeds. The boxes, each containing a different material, were dropped simultaneously from the top of the leaning tower of Pisa, and an attempt was made to detect any difference in the times at which they reached the ground.
>
> So far as could be observed, the boxes all reached the ground simultaneously, irrespective of their contents, and it was concluded therefore that *the acceleration of a body, when falling freely, is independent of the nature of the body.*[12]

Was that the conclusion of the spectators, whom Moore does not openly mention? Arnold does not neglect them:

> [The fact of free fall was proved] by Galileo in his famous experiment at the leaning tower of Pisa, from which he let fall two iron balls of greatly different mass. As they started at the same

[12] H. Moore, *A Textbook of Intermediate Physics*, New York, 1923, p. 52.

instant, they reached the ground together, to the great mystification of onlookers.[13]

'Mystification' is hardly the word, if we are to judge from Ivor B. Hart as introduced by Charles Singer and published by the Oxford University Press. Hart embellishes the traditional account, but has failed to inquire whether Galileo performed his famous experiment from the tower more than once, and also leads us to think that most of the spectators were aged men, hard to assemble, whereas we see from Viviani that most of them must have been young, since according to him the audience included the entire body of students at the University of Pisa. Hart writes:

Galileo's older colleagues knew nothing of experiments. The very idea implied to them a sort of hideous witchcraft—a profanation of the sanctity of the Aristotelian doctrine. One part of the doctrine, it will be remembered, stated that a heavy body will fall to the earth more rapidly than a lighter one. Thus a 100 lb. weight will fall in one-hundredth the time it will take a 1 lb. weight to fall through a given distance. One would scarcely dare claim much pluck or originality for the idea of dropping two such weights simultaneously from a given height in order to put the great Aristotle to the test; yet this simple experiment was in fact one of the outstanding achievements of scientific history. It is astonishing to think that such an experiment had not been deliberately performed for it least two thousand years. Thinkers had come and gone, yet this absurd fiction of the great Greek philosopher had persisted through the ages. And the men who were considered *par excellence* the great minds of the sixteenth century refused the evidence of their own senses! It is a problem for the psychologist.

The story of the experiment at the leaning tower of Pisa is well known. It speaks volumes for the vigorous personality of young

[13] J. Loring Arnold, *Concise Technical Physics*, New York, 1916, p. 16.

Galileo that he got his audience together at all. There is real humor in the thought. What an unwilling audience they must have made! What angry mutterings must have accompanied the preliminaries as this young upstart slowly mounted the tower. [Why 'slowly'?] And then, no doubt, a hush of unwilling expectancy as the signal was given for the simultaneous release of heavy and light weights. Surely it is difficult to believe that these aged philosophers had not, at some time or other in their lives, seen two such weights drop in more or less the same time. [The phrase 'more or less' indicates that Hart never tried the experiment?] They must surely have felt, in their heart of hearts, that they were fighting a losing fight, and that this young firebrand of a Galileo was a true herald of a new era.

Crash! With simultaneous thud those two weights did indeed reach the ground at the same time. It was truly a great moment in the history of the world. Yet the blind prejudice of an unreasoning hero-worship was too strong even for the evidence of the senses of sight and sound. 'Let us go home again,' said they, 'and look it up.' So back they went to their old books, and there sure enough it was— a heavy body falls faster than a lighter body. Besides, and the thought was like balm to their wounded sensibilities, does not the Church sanction the views of the great Aristotle? So the net result of it all was that whilst they secretly feared Galileo, they openly disliked him. It was but the beginning of his career, yet his enemies multiplied rapidly.[14]

Lastly, an author who wishes 'science' to be new has yet somehow got modern diction and concepts like 'one hundred pounds' and 'spell of gravity' transferred back from Newton and Galileo to Aristotle himself. This author, Floyd L. Darrow (1930), is the latest witness I cite:

We remember him [Aristotle] chiefly as the perpetrator of one of the most colossal blunders in the whole history of science. Because

[14] *Makers of Science; Mathematics, Physics, Astronomy;* by Ivor B. Hart, with an Introduction by Dr. Charles Singer, London, Oxford University Press, 1923, pp. 105-6.

it seemed plausible to his unscientific sense of the eternal fitness of things, this Greek speculator unhesitatingly gave the weight of his immense influence to the false assumption that a body weighing one hundred pounds will fall under the spell of gravity one hundred times as fast as a body weighing one pound. Not until the famous experiment of Galileo at the leaning tower of Pisa in the sixteenth century was the ghost of this myth finally laid.[15]

But suppose Galileo did not perform the experiment? What shall we say then about ghosts and myths? It is now time to present a fair translation of the story that Viviani wrote some dozen years after Galileo died; the original passage will, of course, be given later (No. 28). One thing to notice in it is the assertion of Viviani that Galileo made the experiment from the tower repeatedly ('con replicate esperienze'); the oftener he made it about 1590, the stranger the universal silence on the subject until 1654:

At this time, as he seemed to learn that the investigation of natural effects necessarily demanded a knowledge of the nature of motion, granting the philosophic and familiar axiom, *Ignorance of motion spells ignorance of Nature*, he gave himself wholly to the contemplation of this. And then, to the dismay of all the philosophers, very many conclusions of Aristotle were by him [Galileo] proved false through experiments and solid demonstrations and discourses, conclusions which up to then had been held for absolutely clear and indubitable; as, among others, that the velocity of moving bodies of the same material, of unequal weight, moving through the same medium, did *not* mutually preserve the proportion of their weight as taught by Aristotle, but all moved at the same speed; demonstrating this with repeated experiments from the height of the Campanile of Pisa in the presence of the other teachers and philosophers, and the whole assembly of students; and also that the velocity of a given body through different media kept the reciprocal proportion of the

[15] Darrow, *The New World of Physical Discovery*, Indianapolis, 1930, p. 11.

resistance or density of the said media, a point which he deduced from the very obvious absurdities which would [otherwise] follow as a consequence and against reason.

He upheld the dignity of this professorial chair with so great fame and reputation, before judges well-disposed and sincere, that many philosophasters, his rivals, stirred with envy, were aroused against him.

Now we have no contemporary evidence that envy or rancor stirred against Galileo during his brief and early tenure of the chair at Pisa. But, apart from that, are we to suppose that the 'teachers and philosophers,' all of them, and 'the whole body of students' at the University, as Viviani asserts, attended the spectacle of Galileo dropping weights from the leaning tower every time he repeated it? How, indeed, are we now to view the entire story? With a chill, I should think, some of the facile writers we have cited might peruse the considered utterance of Wohlwill, a sceptic concerning the alleged experiment of Galileo, but the best-informed student on all matters concerning the story. Jacopo Mazzoni, whom Wohlwill mentions, was the master and friend who in 1597 published a *Comparison of Aristotle and Plato* in which his pupil Galileo's principles of motion are accepted.[16] Listen to Wohlwill:

As quite without support, then, and improbable, must one regard the story, first recorded more than sixty years later, of the public experiments by which Galileo from the height of the Campanile at Pisa demonstrated to the assembled University students and professors below that large and small bodies of the same sort fall with equal speed. Not a word has Mazzoni to say of these experiments at the point where, in opposition to Aristotle, he circumstantially defends the same thesis. Galileo never mentions them in his records at Pisa, nor when occasion offers in his later writings. And it is equally

[16] *Cf.* Leonardo Olschki, *Galileo und seine Zeit*, 1927, p. 204.

impossible to believe that the fact of that public demonstration was known through personal experience or tradition to the learned Pisans who, twenty years after he [Galileo] had left Pisa, in writings directed against him,[17] attacked as something absolutely new and unheard of his thesis, now first published, of the uniform speed of falling bodies.[18]

First, then, observe that we have no contemporary evidence of any rupture between Galileo and any of his colleagues, or any students, in his short and early period of teaching (1589-91) at Pisa, when he published nothing. Viviani and others have seen Galileo's earlier life too much in the light of disputes that arose after he began to publish. And further, any attack by others upon the views he espoused on falling bodies at first had to deal with publications earlier than his. Thus an argument at once powerful and amusing against our story concerns the absence of allusion by Giorgio Coresio to any such public experiments by Galileo, in the attack Coresio

[17] Compare Coresio in the next passage quoted (p. 29).

[18] 'Als völlig unverbürgt und unwahrscheinlich muss daher auch die mehr als sechzig Jahre später zum ersten Male niedergeschriebene Erzählung von den öffentlichen Versuchen betrachtet werden, durch die Galilei von der Höhe des Pisaner Campanile herab vor der gesamten Studentenschaft und den Professoren der Universität bewiesen haben soll, dass grosse und kleine Körper derselben Art mit gleicher Geschwindigkeit fallen. Auch von diesen Versuchen ist bei Mazzone da, wo er umständlich gegen Aristoteles die gleiche Behauptung verteidigt, nicht die Rede. Galilei selbst hat sie weder in den Pisaner Aufzeichnungen noch bei geeigneter Gelegenheit in späteren Schriften erwähnt, und ebensowenig lässt sich glauben, dass die Tatsache jener öffentlichen Demonstration durch eigene Erfahrung oder Tradition den Pisaner Gelehrten bekannt gewesen ist, die zwanzig Jahre, nachdem er Pisa verlassen, in gegen ihn gerichteten Schriften als etwas völlig Neues und Unerhörtes auch seine damals zuerst veröffentlichte Behauptung von der gleichen Fallgeschwindigkeit bekämpften.' Thus Emil Wohlwill, *Galilei und sein Kampf für die Copernicanische Lehre*, Hamburg und Leipzig, 1909, 1.115; cf. ibid. 2 (1926). 282-94. See also Wohlwill, *Galilei-Studien*, 1. *Die Pisaner Fallversuche*, in *Mitteilungen z. Geschichte d. Medizin u. d. Naturwissenschaften* 4 (1905). 229-48; Leonardo Olschki in rebuttal (*Bildung und Wissenschaft im Zeitalter der Renaissance in Italien* 2 (1922). 254-5) is not convincing.

made in 1612 upon the aforesaid doctrines of Mazzoni which were published in 1597. Galileo had left Pisa for a less meagre income, and with a better stipend became professor at the University of Padua. There he taught for eighteen years, until he moved to Florence in 1610. He certainly ascended the tower of St. Mark's at Venice on August 21, 1609, in order to demonstrate his telescope, not to demonstrate the fall of bodies; that is historical fact. Well then, in 1612 Coresio suggests that Mazzoni had experimented with falling bodies, but from an insufficient height; and avers that he, Coresio, by due experiment from the tower of Pisa had demonstrated the truth of Aristotle's statement concerning the relative speed of their fall!

Mazzoni [says Coresio] commits anew two other errors of no slight importance. First, he denies a matter of experiment, that, with one and the same material, the whole moves more swiftly than the part. Herein his mistake arose because, perhaps, he made his experiment from his window, and because the window was low all his heavy substances went down evenly. But *we* did it from the top of the cathedral tower of Pisa, actually testing the statement of Aristotle that the whole of the same material in a figure proportional to the part descends more quickly than the part. The place, in truth, was very suitable, since, if there were wind, it could by its impulse alter the result; but in that place there could be no such danger. And thus was confirmed the statement of Aristotle, in the first book of *De Caelo*, that the larger body of the same material moves more swiftly than the smaller, and in proportion as the weight increases so does the velocity.[19]

[19] Coresio, *Operetta intorno al Galleggiare de Corpi Solidi*, Firenze, 1612; in Galileo, *Opere*, Ed. Naz., 4.242: 'Commette di nuovo due altri errori il Mazzoni, non di poco momento: il primo, negando l'esperienza che in una medesima materia si muova il tutto più presto della parte. Nella quale s'ingannò, perchè ne fece forse l'esperienza dalla sua finestra, la quale perchè fu bassa, da essa tutte le materie gravi andarono forse ugualmente a basso; ma noi l'abbiamo

Surely Wohlwill is right. If Galileo had openly and repeatedly experimented from the tower of Pisa while teaching in the local University, some mention of the fact would be made in the dispute of 1612. Again, in the year 1641, in the friendly correspondence between Galileo, at Arcetri, and Vincenzo Renieri, now for some months past tenant of the chair of mathematics at Pisa which Galileo had held fifty years earlier, there would be the best of opportunities for reference to Galileo and the leaning tower, and there is never a hint that he engaged in the alleged experiments. It is Renieri who in March, 1641, has just had a hand in such experiments from the tower, gives Galileo the news of them, and asks for Galileo's interpretation of what seemingly occurred. It appears that Renieri hitherto had but cursorily looked at Galileo's *Dialogues concerning Two New Sciences* (1638). In an intervening letter which is lost, Galileo refers him to that work for the answer to inquiries about the speed of falling bodies. Renieri in a second letter promises to study the volume with care. What more Galileo may have wished of him we cannot say; but in the absence of the lost letter we have to infer from all the implications of the two extant letters that nothing was said by either correspondent of any experiments ever performed by Galileo from the tower. There is simply no evidence that

---

fatta di cima al campanile del Duomo di Pisa, esperimentando vero il detto d'Aristotile, che 'l tutto della medesima materia in figura proporzionata alla parte discendeva più velocemente di essa: luogo veramente a proposito fu, poi che il vento, mediante l'impulsione, potrebbe variare l'effetto, nel qual luogo non sarebbe mai tal pericolo. E così viene avverato il detto d'Aristotile nel primo del Cielo, che'l corpo maggiore si muove più velocemente del minore della medesima materia, e nel medesimo modo che cresce la gravità, cresce ancora la velocità.'

the younger man ever heard of them; it is hardly conceivable that, if he had, he would fail to allude to them. Moreover, the views of Renieri which Galileo in 1641 sought to correct are evidence enough that no 'epoch-making' and general advance in the study of free fall could be sharply dated from Galileo's brief tenure, when he was young, of the chair at Pisa. The letter of Renieri dated from Pisa, March 13, 1641, I translate almost entire, giving all that bears upon our question:

We have had occasion here to make experiment of two weights falling from a height, of diverse material, namely one of wood and one of lead, but of the same size; because a certain Jesuit [Niccolò Cabeo] writes that they descend in the same time, and with equal velocity reach the earth; and a certain Englishman affirms that Liceti here set a problem, and gave the explanation of it. But finally we have found the fact in the contrary, because from the summit of the Campanile of the Cathedral [at Pisa], between the ball of lead and the ball of wood there occur at least three cubits of difference. Experiments also were made with two balls of lead, one of a bigness equal to a cannon-ball and the other to a musket-ball, and there was observed between the biggest and the smallest, from the height of the same Campanile, to be a good palm's difference by which the biggest preceded the smallest. What was noted by me in such experiments was this: it struck me that, the motion of the wooden balls being accelerated down to a certain mark, they began then not to descend perpendicularly but obliquely in the same manner as we see drops of water do as they fall from roofs, the which, coming near to the earth, swerve aside, and here their motion begins to be less rapid. I have thought about this a little, and shall give your Excellency my notion of it.

If we suppose that a moving body moves through a definite medium, then the velocity with which it can pass through the medium must also be definite, so that if one wished to make it go faster, the medium would resist one through its not being able to yield and give place so quickly. For example, I shall move a fan with little effort if I move it with little impetus, but if I wish to move it with great force, I shall perceive resistance made to me from the air, and even to the point of interference with my motion of it. That being granted, when the ball of wood starts from the height, moving with little velocity and constantly accelerating more and more, it finally arrives at such a stage that the air can make resistance to it, and the heavy body, not being able to cleave the medium perpendicularly, hangs and swerves to one side, and then perchance, beginning again to descend more swiftly, again will begin to be retarded; after the fashion in which a sheet of paper goes through the air, swerving now to the right, now to the left, before it manages to descend to the ground. I don't now know if the lead falling from a very great height could attain to such a rate of velocity that the same thing could be seen in it. Your Excellency might give a little thought to this, and will bear with me if perchance I have failed to make myself clear in the present letter, since I happen to have written in haste because of returning home late.[20]

Galileo, it is clear, answered promptly, though his answer now is missing. The second letter I translate from Renieri almost in its entirety; it followed the first by a week, and is dated, also from Pisa, March 20, 1641:

Your Excellency's last Dialogue has not been read by me save here and there, because last summer, when I might have given diligent attention to it, you know how I was placed, and since then I have not had time to be able to examine it with such care as the demonstrations which are in it demand. I know it is most true that two heavy bodies differing in kind, equal however in mass, do not preserve any proportion of weight in their descent, nay rather that, for example, in water wood will move contrariwise to lead; and so from the very outset I laughed at the experiment [or 'experience'] of the Jesuit [Niccolò Cabeo] who affirmed that the lead *and a*

[20] *Ed. Naz.* 18.305-6; see below, No. 26.

crumb of bread (to speak as he writes) move with equal velocity to the centre; but that two heavy bodies, unequal in weight but of the same material, falling from the same height perpendicularly have to arrive with different velocity and in different time at the centre, this I think I have heard or read from you—but don't well remember—cannot be. However, in these few days of vacation I shall read your last Dialogue, although the complete perusal of it I must reserve for myself to do with more ease this coming summer. Meanwhile we shall return to making experiments with the balls, and see if we were mistaken the first time in the observation that when they neared the earth they swerved, and did not go perpendicularly; and I shall inform your Excellency about this.[21]

These two letters of Renieri, then, confirm the view of Wohlwill that Galileo did not experiment with falling bodies from the Pisan Campanile.

My citation of Wohlwill and Olschki now leads me to tell why I undertook to write on this theme. So far as I could learn with the help of friends who are well-versed in physical science or in the Renaissance, there was no published article or book in English where amateurs like myself could study the evidence on this tale of Aristotle, Galileo, and the leaning tower, and no publication at all where specialists with but limited access to foreign or ancient books could do so. Further, I have had some experience with the difficulties of interpreting Aristotle—mainly, however, in works other than his *Physics* or *De Caelo*—and some other experience in making or judging translations; at all events experience enough, I hope, whether in the classical or the modern languages, to warrant my attempting this simple task. I here aim to assemble in English the passages requisite to a physicist, say, who would

[21] *Ed. Naz.* 18.310; see below, No. 27.

like to form his own opinion about this story; to include, I think for the first time with the story, a collection of passages from Aristotle, who has not been well treated by admirers of Galileo; and finally, in order to give my compilation a scholarly or scientific value, to append an ample list of passages in the original.

Before going further with this task, however, I must include other preliminary remarks, some quoted from good commentators—such as Platt and Ross on Aristotle—or derived from trustworthy writers, particularly Wohlwill, on the historical background of Galileo, and some of my own which are offered with more hesitation than may appear on the surface; yet I am sure the technical reader will forgive my lack of training in physics, and forgive such results of that lack as do not disturb our principal aim.

On the occasional difficulty of interpreting the style of Aristotle we may hearken to one of his translators, Platt:

In extracting his [Aristotle's] meaning it is often necessary to go behind the fragmentary and obscure wording of his statements and see what was really in his mind. The treatises of Aristotle are often of the nature of note-books for lectures; he puts down sentences intelligible to himself which he can amplify and make clear, but which by themselves are bewildering fragments. Besides this they have suffered terribly in the process of transmission to us, and are full of grievous blunders committed by scribes; whole passages have often fallen out, and we can only guess what was in them; other bits have been added by people too ignorant to avoid supplying nonsense for sense. In fact, when we come across a really thorny passage we can only deal with it if we have undergone a long and special training in Aristotelian scholarship, which is an art by itself.[22]

[22] Arthur Platt, *Aristotle on the Heart*, in *Studies in the History and Method of Science*, ed. by Charles Singer, Oxford, 1921, 2.521.

Platt's confession should be a warning to all who talk glibly about Aristotle's 'unscientific sense' of the fitness of things. And the editor of the great Oxford translation of Aristotle, who has been at work upon a commentary on the *Physics*, should give all of us pause when he writes thus of a word that must lie at the heart of any discussion about the difference between ancient and modern views of motion:

Many of the technical terms in the *Physics* present considerable difficulties to the translator. The most difficult, perhaps, is κίνησις· κίνησις would often be most aptly rendered by 'change'; but often again it is distinguished from μεταβολή, and therefore narrower than 'change.' As the lesser of two evils, I have adopted the translation 'motion' or 'movement,' and have very rarely departed from this; this rendering should be recognized as being to some extent conventional.[23]

Another expression of Aristotle which may cause difficulty is τὰ φερόμενα, which is likely to be translated as 'moving bodies,' but, more strictly considered, means 'moved bodies,' 'bodies borne along.' Further, we must not forget that the concept of 'inertia' is strictly modern. On this point, a fuller discussion of which would lie beyond my competence, I refer to the treatise of Deshayes, *La Découverte de l'Inertie, Essai sur les Lois Générales du Mouvement de Platon à Galilee*, Paris, 1930. And here perhaps may be mentioned another study, by Kurt Lewin, *Der Uebergang von der Aristotelischen zur Galileischen Denkweise in Biologie und Psychologie*, which appeared in *Erkenntnis zugleich Annalen der Philosophie* 1 (1931).421-66, and also, translated into English, in the *Journal of General Psychology* 5 (1931).141-77. This article

[23] W. D. Ross, Preface to the *Physics*, in *The Works of Aristotle, translated into English* 2 (1930). iii-iv.

or address, whatever its general value may be, is characterized by its lack of specific reference to passages in the works either of Aristotle or of Galileo.

To continue a discussion of special terms. If, in the passages Stevin, Galileo, and others before them, attacked, Aristotle does not use the word 'fall,' what word does he use? It is ῥοπή, not identical with *velocitas*, but a more general term like 'impulse' or 'momentum'; in a Latin translation of *De Caelo* which was familiar to the Renaissance, that by John Argyropylos of Byzantium (1416-86), for example in the significant passage 3.2.301ª20 ff., the Greek word is rendered by 'momentum.' As directly connected with verb ῥέπειν, to *incline* this way or that, ῥοπή is associated with the action of a pair of scales; so that, when Aristotle thought of a heavy body trending downwards faster than a light one, if he was not thinking of their behavior in our hands, he may at times have had in mind the sudden descent of the scales on one side when a heavier body is there substituted for a lighter. Or on occasion he may have used two pairs of scales to note the ῥοπή or downward inclination of two pieces of metal as compared with each other; he doubtless was familiar with two types of scales discussed in *Mechanica* 1.849ᵇ19-850ª2 and 20.853ᵇ25-854ª15, though this work seems not to be Aristotle's. Bonitz regards ῥοπή as 'inclination downwards,' or 'that which causes inclination downwards.' But with Aristotle ῥοπή means trend or tendency upward as well,[24] and he would use this word for the tendency upward of a large portion of air through water, or of a large portion of fire upward through air; and with respect to the law of motion

[24] Cf. *Physics* 4.8.216ª13-14; below, No. 12.

which Galileo and others combated, we should recall that
Aristotle would apply ῥοπή to all four of the elements which he
recognized, namely, fire, air, water, and earth. That he was
justified at his time in regarding fire, for example, as an
element may be granted when we think of a modern belief
in phlogiston, which hardly died out before the year 1800.
Accordingly, it need not seem strange if he thought that a
large body of fire, a large flame, trended upward through air
faster than a small one. It is true, he conceives this law of
motion in such general terms that we should not discuss it
too much in terms of up and down;[25] we remember that the
passages Galileo and the rest attacked were mainly or entirely
concerned with Aristotle's argument against 'the void' of the
Atomists, that is, against the possibility of a true vacuum, and
not with questions of 'up' and 'down.' It is perhaps worth note
that a traditional diagram illustrating *De Caelo* 3.2, found
in the sixth-century commentary of Simplicius, represents the
motions of the heavy and the light body, not by vertical, but
by horizontal lines.[26] Aristotle rules out 'the void' or vacuum;
a moving object therefore moves through a medium that
tends to impede it, and the lighter the body, the more effective
is the check. We may say that the lighter bodies are the faster
they rise; but, strictly speaking, though Aristotle in *De Caelo*
uses the words 'up' (ἄνω) and 'down' (κάτω) freely, the
motions he has in mind are *away from the centre*, and *toward
the centre*, rather than straight up and down to us where we

[25] Before Aristotle, Plato's Timaeus has an argument against speaking of
'up' and 'down' in relation to infinite space; see *Timaeus* 62 d. The Atomists
had trouble with the notion; see Cyril Bailey, *The Greek Atomists and
Epicurus*, p. 312.
[26] *Simplicii in Aristotelis De Caelo Commentaria*, ed. I. L. Heiberg, Berlin,
1893, p. 592; see below, No. 14.

stand—are on an infinite number of lines oblique to this, not merely on this line.

Of course, if he expresses himself in general terms, we can illustrate his law in many specific ways, for example: 'If you were to drop two balls of gold, one ten times the weight of the other, into loose earth, the heavier would in the same interval penetrate into the thin medium, the loose earth, farther in direct proportion to its weight.' True, he nowhere gives this illustration, nor talks about going up to a height and dropping things down. But it would be as fair to assert what I have affected to quote as it is for the respectable Fahie to assert what we have read above: 'Aristotle had said that, if two different weights of the same material were let fall from the same height, the two would reach the ground in a period of time inversely proportional to their weights.' Doubtless the nearest approach by Aristotle to saying that is an utterance, again incidental to another argument, on the question whether the earth itself is at rest or in motion: 'It would indeed be a complacent mind that felt no surprise that, while a little bit of earth, let loose in mid-air, moves and will not stay still, and the more there is of it the faster it moves, the whole earth, free in mid-air, should show no movement at all.'[27]

As we have seen, and shall see, it is pretty clear that writers like Fahie have not studied what Aristotle actually says about the motions of earth, air, fire, and water, or about hypothetical movement in a vacuum.[28] I am afraid that what he does say

---

[27] Aristotle *De Caelo* 2.13.294ª12-16 in Stocks' translation; see below, No. 4.
[28] Compare Wicksteed in Aristotle, *The Physics* (Loeb Classical Library) 1.356-7: 'It is tantalizing to find Aristotle actually arriving at the fact, familiar in modern laboratories, that a feather and a guinea, to take the classical example,

lies open to the test of Stevin, and that it had been found vulnerable in antiquity; and shall now give two passages that are as damaging as any to Aristotle in the light of the traditional test. The first is from *De Caelo* 4.2.309ª27-ᵇ18:

But those who attribute the lightness of fire to its containing so much void are necessarily involved in practically the same difficulties. For though fire be supposed to contain less solid than any other body, as well as more void, yet there will be a certain quantum of fire in which the amount of solid or plenum is in excess of the solids contained in some small quantity of earth. They may reply that there is an excess of void also. But the question is, how will they discriminate the absolutely heavy? Presumably, either by its excess of solid or by its defect of void. On the former view there could be an amount of earth so small as to contain less solid than a large mass of fire. And similarly, if the distinction rests on the amount of void, there will be a body, lighter than the absolutely light, which nevertheless moves downward as constantly as the other moves upward. But that cannot be so, since the absolutely light is always lighter than bodies which have weight and move downward, while, on the other hand, that which is lighter need not be light, because in common speech we distinguish a lighter and a heavier (viz. water and earth) among bodies endowed with weight. Again, the suggestion of a certan ratio between the void and the solid in a body is no more equal to solving the problem before us. This manner of speaking will issue in a similar impossibility. For any two portions of fire, small or great, will exhibit the same ratio of solid to void; but the upward movement of the greater is quicker than that of the less, just as the downward movement of a mass of gold or lead, or of any other body endowed with weight, is quicker in proportion to its size. This, however, should not be the case if the ratio is the ground of distinction between heavy things and light. There is also an absurdity in attributing the upward movement of bodies to a void which does not itself move.[29]

will fall at the same pace through a vacuum, but treating it as a *reductio ad absurdum.'*

[29] Stocks' translation, see below, No. 7.

The next passage has a special interest because it is associated with the earliest attack we know of upon Aristotle for his views on the subject we are discussing. It is taken from the *Physics* 4.8.216ª8-21 in the Oxford translation (1930), edited by Ross:

To sum the matter up, the cause of this result is obvious, viz. that between any two movements there is a ratio (for they occupy time, and there is a ratio between any two times, so long as both are finite), but there is no ratio of void to full.

These are the consequences that result from a difference in the media; the following depend upon an excess of one moving [or 'moved'] body over another. We see that bodies which have a greater impulse ['trend,' 'momentum'] either of weight or of lightness, if they are alike in other respects, move faster over an equal space, and in the ratio which their magnitudes bear to each other. Therefore they will also move through the void with this ratio of speed. But that is impossible; for why should one move faster? (In moving through *plena* it must be so; for the greater divides them faster by its force. For a moving thing cleaves the medium either by its shape or by the impulse which the body that is carried along or is projected possesses.) Therefore all will possess equal velocity. But this is impossible.[30]

[30] See below, No. 12. This is in the part of the *Physics* that has aroused the traditional opposition to Aristotle for his views on falling bodies; see the sixth-century commentary of Philoponus (below, p. 47 and passage No. 13). Aristotle's words as translated above immediately become more vulnerable in our eyes when we import into them the notions of up and down which the Oxford translators very properly do not find in the Greek. Observe the change when the translator's notions creep into his rendering; so Wicksteed in the Loeb Classical Library: 'But . . . as to differences that depend on the moving bodies themselves, we see that of two bodies of similar formation the one that has the stronger trend downward by weight or upward by buoyancy, as the case may be, will be carried more quickly than the other through a given space in proportion to the greater strength of this trend. And this should hold in vacancy as elsewhere. But it cannot; for what reason can be assigned for this greater velocity?'

There we doubtless have the passage that has been at the centre of the attack upon Aristotle with respect to free fall; and with respect to falling bodies it is vulnerable; but as the opponents of Aristotle's followers in the Renaissance (and doubtless far earlier) made their attack, they were unfair. They did not reckon with the cases in which Aristotle's generalization was supported by what were to him facts, and did not consider how the special case they picked on was related to his argument on 'the void.' They wanted scientific and historical perspective. In our day, however, should we not expect writers on the development of science to observe the injunction of Agassiz? 'In dealing with the history of a subject,' he told Wilder, 'the value of each successive contribution should be estimated in the light of the knowledge at the period, not of that at the present time.'[31] And compare what Dingler, in a review of Dijksterhuis, says in defence of Aristotle:

I would only observe that perhaps the commonly accepted theoretical point of view in science to-day . . . is not the final one, and hence that criticisms based upon it may subsequently need revision. For myself, I believe it possible that from another point of view one could understand the procedure of Aristotle so well from his situation that there would be simply no place left for blame.[32]

[31] Cooper, *Louis Agassiz as a Teacher*, 1917, p. 39.
[32] Hugo Dingler, review of Dijksterhuis, E. J., *Val en Worp; een Bijdrage tot de Geschiedenis der Mechanica van Aristoteles tot Newton;* in *Mitteilungen z. Geschichte d. Medizin u. d. Naturwissenschaften* 24 (1925). 147: 'Ich wollte nur hinweisen, dass vielleicht auch der heute verbreitete wissenschaftstheoretische Standpunkt (dem auch der Verf. huldigt) nicht der letzte ist, und dass daher von ihm aus vorgenommene Kritiken später einer Revision bedürftig werden könnten. Ich persönlich glaube, dass man von einem anderen Standpunkt aus das Verfahren des Aristoteles so wohl aus seiner Situation verstehen könnte, dass zu einem Tadel überhaupt kein Platz mehr wäre.'

Then historical perspective is needed for the positions of Aristotle which were assailed by Galileo. Galileo himself, of course, was not an impartial historian of science. In contrast with men like Leonardo, who experimented freely, Galileo, though he did indeed experiment, is on one side an observer, like Aristotle, of what actually happens, on another a desk-mathematician like Kepler. At one point Galileo says, in words which I reserve for the end of my argument, that he had repeatedly performed an experiment which it seems to us he could not have performed, showing that a piece of wood let fall from a high tower begins to fall faster than a piece of lead.[33] His general habit of contemplation argues against Viviani's story about the repeated experiments from the tower of Pisa. Galileo was perhaps more likely to watch a pendulum that was already swinging, and to climb a tower only for the sake of his telescope, though the story of the pendulum seems also to have gone the way of Newton's apple, while his use of the telescope in the tower at Venice remains historical fact. But he was not over-contemplative in his personal dealings or his attitude to tradition; and his perspective in history was none the better for a certain tragic impatience in him, which, like the flaw in a noble hero of the drama, brought upon him sufferings out of proportion to his zeal for justice. In youth Galileo adhered to the physics of Aristotle as Aristotle was then understood, and throughout his career at Padua—certainly in 1606, and clearly after he was privately convinced of the truth in Copernicus' view of the solar system—he continued to present the Ptolemaic system of the heavens in his university lectures. Yet, once he

[33] See below, pp. 54-5, and passage No. 23.

had to his own satisfaction upset the supposed contention of
Aristotle as to falling bodies, Galileo's reaction to it betrays
the animus of one who has outgrown an error, and now
detects this error as a kind of vulgarity in his rivals. In order
to abash the 'Aristotelians' of his prime, Galileo, like
Bruno, and like many another intense individualist of the
Renaissance, becomes unjust to Aristotle. Then, as later, but
few estimates of the Greek writer steered fairly between the
extremes of adulation and censure; even in our day few persons reckon aright with some inevitable limitations of Aristotle in his time, and manage to do justice to his extraordinary
attainments, his good sense constantly mounting to wisdom,
his services, beyond those of any one else we know, in found-
ing and promoting diverse branches of science, his permanent,
still solid, contributions, great and small, to most of the
departments of human learning. If I am not mistaken, the
competent and fair-minded reader of our day who will
compare the Oxford translation of the *Physics* and *De Caelo*,
first with anything on the subject before Aristotle, and then
with a modern writer like Jeans or Eddington, will promptly
admit that, so far as records enable us to speak, the scientific
attitude to physics begins with Aristotle and no other man.
Galileo, probably to his own harm, once he had broken
inwardly with an early adherence to Aristotle, never again
in his heart, so far as I can judge, found anything to approve
in this very illuminating author.[34]

Yet, in turning from one tradition, Galileo in fact merely
turned to another. Thus the passages from *De Caelo* and the

[34] Among my notes I find a speech of 'Salviati' (*Ed. Naz.* 7.75) referred
to as an apparent exception to this statement; but a study of the next speech,
by 'Simplicio,' shows it to be no exception.

Physics which we find him assailing in his manuscript studies *De Motu,* written about 1590, were already the conventional, even traditional, passages to attack. Stevin may have been ready to impugn them in 1586, though his first reference to them appears, not in his work of that date, *De Beghinselen der Weeghkonst,* published at Leyden, but, as we have seen above, in 1605; for Stevin notes earlier objectors, Jean Taisnier and Jerome Cardan. Now Taisnier was more than heavily indebted to Giovanni Battista Benedetti;[35] while Benedetti, who owed much to Leonardo da Vinci, became in turn a source for Galileo's master, Mazzoni, and for Galileo. We may note that Galileo's *De Motu,* though of a date about 1590, and accessible in manuscript to Viviani in 1654, was not published until 1883, and that Galileo himself published nothing before 1606.[36] His famous *Dialogues concerning Two New Sciences* saw the light in 1638; here two of the speakers adduced laws of motion on which Galileo had touched in his unpublished treatise *De Motu.* With these dates in mind, we may list the names of persons writing before Galileo published anything, who either presumptively and according to belief,

[35] Wohlwill, *Galilei* 1.90, calls Taisnier a 'shameless plagiarist' of Benedetti; and rightly, according to present standards. See *Demonstratio Proportionum Motuum localium contra Aristotelem et alios Philosophos. Ad pium et non aemulum Lectorem Ioannes Taisnier Hannonius*—pp. 16-17 of his *Opusculum Perpetua Memoria Dignissimum* [etc.], Coloniae, Apud Ioannem Birckmannum, Anno M.D.LXII. In the *Demonstratio,* pp. 21-22, Taisnier, following Benedetti, cites, I think, all the passages Stevin and Galileo cite from Aristotle in proving him wrong about the speed of falling bodies. Benedetti evidently read Archimedes *De Incidentibus Aquae.*

[36] In a letter to Guidobaldo del Monte, Nov. 29, 1602 (*Ed. Naz.* 10.97-100), Galileo discusses the descent of heavy bodies along the arcs of circles; and in a letter to Paolo Sarpi, Oct. 16, 1604 (*Ed. Naz.* 10.115-6), he discusses the free fall of heavy bodies. According to Wohlwill, *Galilei* 2.281, it was in 1604, or not much earlier, that Galileo derived or determined the laws of falling bodies.

or certainly, took issue with the notion that bodies fall with a speed proportional to their weight. In addition to the names and the date of birth or death or both, I give, where possible, the date of a significant writing.

Simon Stevin, 1548-1620, pub. 1605;[37] Jacopo Mazzoni, 1548-98, pub. 1597; Francesco Piccolomini, 1520-1604, pub. *Liber Scientiae de Natura* 1597; Cardan, 1501?-76, pub. *De Proportionibus* 1570; Taisnier, b. 1508, pub. *Opusculum* (with *Demonstratio* plagiarized from Benedetti) 1562; G. B. Bellaso, pub. *Il vero Modo di Scrivere in Cifra* [etc.], Venice, 1553, 1567, Brescia, 1564;[38] Giovanni Battista Benedetti, 1530-90, pub. *Demonstratio Proportionum Motuum localium contra Aristotelem et omnes Philosophos* (?) 1553, Venice, 1554, and *Diversarum Speculationum mathematicarum et physicarum Liber*, Turin, 1585 (reissued 1599); Niccolò Tartaglia, 1499-1557, pub. *Quesiti et Inventioni diversi*, Venice, 1546, and Latin translation of parts of the works of Archimedes, Venice, 1543; Benedetto Varchi, composed *Questione sull' Alchemia* 1544 (printed at Florence, 1827);[39] Francesco Beato, about the time of Varchi;

[37] Galileo mentions Stevin once, *Ed. Naz.* 5.62, in a colorless way. Stevin (see my first paragraph, and below, passage No. 19) says that he and Grotius refuted Aristotle '*quondam*'—implying at least a good many years before 1605.

[38] According to Roberto Marcolongo (*Atti della R. Accademia dei Lincei, Memorie della Classe di Scienze fisiche, matematiche, e naturali* 13 (1920). 114), the Brescia edition (of 16 pages) contains, among cryptographic propositions, 'La ragione perchè lassando cadere da alto à basso due palle, una di ferro, et l'altra di legno, così presto cada in terra quella di legno, come quella di ferro' ('Why when you let fall from above downwards two balls, one of iron and the other of wood, the one of wood falls to earth as fast as the one of iron').

[39] Marcolongo, *ibid.*, p. 113, quotes Varchi who opposes Aristotle on the point, 'che quanto una cosa sia più grave, tanto più tosto discenda, il che la prova dimostra non esser vero' ('that the heavier a thing is, the quicker it descends, which the test proves not to be true').

Luca Ghini, also about the time of Varchi;[40] Domenicus Soto, 1494-1560; Leonardo da Vinci, 1452-1519; Nicolaus Oresmius, c.1323-82; Jean Buridan, 1300-c.1358; John Philoponus, A.D. (?) 470- (?) 540, or *floruit* first third of the sixth century; Hipparchus c. 160-129 B.C.

It must not be supposed that Leonardo and others consistently upheld our present theory; I have put him into the list mainly on the opinion of Hart, though Leonardo refers with approval to Aristotle, Albertus Magnus, and Aquinas, *De Caelo*.[41] A man might express himself as Aristotle did on the void, and at another time be aware through observation how two different weights behave when falling. If at some time Aristotle were aware of it, he would not be more inconsistent than was Galileo, who at Padua for years continued teaching the conventional stellar and terrestrial physics.[42]

Roger Bacon, 1214-94, is not in our list; he produced *Questions* about four books of Aristotle's *Physics*, but I find no hint that he raised our question. For us the significant names in the list are John Philoponus and, doubtless, Hipparchus. Philoponus was working at his commentary on Aristotle's *Physics* in A.D. 533; that cannot be far from the year when he said, countering a point in Aristotle's argument against the possibility of a vacuum:

[40] Varchi mentions Beato, Professor of Metaphysics at Pisa, and Ghini of Bologna, as among those in his day who made known the mistake of Aristotle about the speed of falling bodies; see Olschki, *Bildung und Wissenschaft* [etc.] 1.131.

[41] See the passage quoted from Hart, below, No. 17, and Leonardo, *Codex Atlanticus*, fol. 123r (below, No. 16). Cf. Albertus Magnus, *Opera* 2 (Lyon, 1651), *De Caelo et Mundo*, Tract. 1, cap. 6, pp. 156-7; Aquinas, *Opera Omnia* 3 (Rome, 1886). 249, *De Caelo et Mundo* 3, cap. 2, Lect. 7.

[42] Cf. Wohlwill, *Galilei* 1.211.

Here is something absolutely false, and something we can better test by observed fact than by any demonstration through logic. If you take two masses greatly differing in weight, and release them from the same elevation, you will see that the ratio of times in their movements does not follow the ratio of the weights, but the difference in time is extremely small; so that if the weights do not greatly differ, but one, say, is double the other, the difference in the times will be either none at all or imperceptible.[43]

It is not likely that the laborious John conceived of the experiment by himself, or performed it; but much more likely that this particular test of a statement of Aristotle goes back to the Alexandrian sources upon which he depends, and at least to the later, more narrowly practical, stage of physical science to which Hipparchus belongs. Simplicius (second quarter of the sixth century), to some extent contemporary with Philoponus, mentions in his commentary on Aristotle *De Caelo* a work in which Hipparchus took issue with the views of Aristotle 'on bodies carried downwards through weight.'[44] But indeed so simple a question concerning the free fall of bodies must have been child's play to Archimedes two centuries before Hipparchus. In the treatise *On Floating Bodies*, Book 1, Proposition 7,[45] it seems clear that Archimedes knew how bodies of the same substance but different weights behave when immersed in water; in fact, the whole treatise is of such a nature that he must have known how such bodies

---

[43] I translate from *Ioannis Philoponi in Aristotelis Physicorum Libros Quinque Posteriores Commentaria*, ed. Vitelli, in *Commentaria in Aristotelem Graeca*, ed. consilio et auctoritate Academiae Litterarum Regiae Borussicae 17 (1888). 683; see below, passage No. 13.

[44] Περὶ τῶν διὰ βαρύτητα κάτω φερομένων. See *Simplicii in Aristotelis De Caelo Commentaria*, ed. Heiberg, in *Commentaria in Aristotelem Graeca*, ed. consilio et auctoritate Academiae Litterarum Regiae Borussicae 7 (1894). 264-5.

[45] Heath, *The Works of Archimedes*, p. 258.

descend; though he is thought by Heath to have had no predecessors in hydrostatics,[46] his work to my mind makes that of Stevin and Galileo look rather amateurish. And, again, the speed of stones and tools, heavy and light, simultaneously falling from a scaffold or ledge while a structure like the Parthenon or the tower of Pisa was building, must have been observed by nearly every mason from the time of the tower of Babel down. And there was tearing down of buildings in the Italian Renaissance, as always everywhere.

Before we come to our collection of illustrative passages, I wish to touch on four other points that may bear upon our subject. The first is the possible Latin influence on the traditional views regarding free fall; the second is the references made by Galileo to experiment as a test of the statements by Aristotle which he combats; the third is some references made by Aristotle to experiments; and the fourth is the very strange assertion made by Galileo in his early treatise *De Motu* that in free fall wood starts off more quickly than lead.

(1) The Latin influence may easily be forgotten, but should always be reckoned with in any discussion of a traditional view that is alive in the Renaissance; for, as a return to the ancient

---

[46] *Ibid.*, p. xi. The *Editio princeps* of Archimedes' *Opera* (*Graece et Latine*) was published at Basel in 1554, edited by Venatorius. Tartaglia's Latin translation of certain of the works of Archimedes, published at Venice in 1543, included: *De centris gravium vel de aequerepentibus* I-II, *Tetragonismus* [*parabolae*], *Dimensio circuli*, and *De insidentibus aquae* I. The rest of Tartaglia's translation (= Book 2 of *De insidentibus aquae*) was published with Book 1 of the same treatise (after his death in 1557) by Troianus Curtius at Venice in 1565. Wohlwill, *Ein Vorgänger Galileis im 6. Jahrhundert* in *Physikalische Zeitschrift* 7 (1906). 23-32, suggests that Galileo's issue with Aristotle should be traced back to Hipparchus; I suggest that it may well go back to Archimedes, if not to the Academy.

classics, the Renaissance was a return to Latin ideals more than Greek. This Roman bias is less noticeable in the realm of physical science, where the Romans did not shine, yet we see that the view about falling bodies that is commonly attributed to Aristotle was kept alive also by the poem of Lucretius, and that means by a Latin exponent of the Greek Atomists whom Aristotle attacked for their belief in the possibility of a vacuum. Lucretius, of course, is dependent upon Epicurus, who is later than Aristotle. Epicurus is dependent upon Democritus, who with Leucippus is assailed by Aristotle; the views of the Greek Atomists on falling bodies form too large a subject for discussion here, and I can include only a little about them in the illustrative passages. So also the original passage from Lucretius, *De Rerum Natura* 2.230-9, will be given later (No. 1); I here subjoin the translation of it by Cyril Bailey:

All things that fall [*cadunt*] through the water and thin air, these things must needs quicken their fall [*casus celerare*] in proportion to their weights [*pro ponderibus*], just because the body of water and the thin nature of air cannot check each thing equally, but give place more quickly when overcome by heavier bodies. But, on the other hand, the empty void cannot . . . support anything; . . . wherefore all things must needs be borne on through the calm void, moving at equal rate with unequal weights.

We note the word 'fall' in the Latin tradition.

(2) There are two passages in which Galileo mentions experiment or experience as a test of Aristotle on our point; in neither does he say that he performed the experiment; one of these (*a*) is early (1590), and contains the expression 'a high tower,' while the other (*b*) is late (1638), and contains

no such expression. And there are four other early passages[47] in which he mentions experiment from a 'tower' or 'high tower' with respect to falling bodies, but these four concern different points from ours, and three of them contain queer notions to us about the initial speed of objects light and heavy. The five early references (and one of them, *Ed. Naz.* 1.334, in particular), since they were accessible in 1654 to Viviani, probably represent the basis of his story concerning the demonstration before the teachers and students in Pisa. In his confusing account, Viviani mentions 'experiments,' 'demonstrations,' and 'discourses'; we readily see that Galileo's early allusions to experiment with falling bodies are in the treatise *De Motu,* which consists of demonstrations, and in the contemporary dialogue *De Motu,* which could properly in Italian be called a *discorso.* The thing that Galileo says he observed, in experiments that he avers he did repeatedly make, will be interesting news to most of my readers, and hence is reserved for a place near the end of these remarks. The first passage, accordingly, which we call *a,* and give now, is from his treatise *De Motu:*

How ridiculous is this opinion of Aristotle is clearer than light. Who ever would believe, for example, that if two spheres of lead were let go from the orb of the moon, one a hundred times greater than the other, and the greater reached the earth in an hour, the less would take a hundred hours in its motion? Or if two stones were flung at the same moment from a high tower, one stone twice the size of the other, who would believe that when the smaller was half-way down the larger had already reached the ground?[48]

[47] *Ed. Naz.* 1.273,329,334,406-7. The first three, like passage *a* (1.263) are in the treatise *De Motu;* the last passage (1.406-7) is in the early dialogue *De Motu* of about the same date.

[48] *Ed. Naz.* 1.263; a more inclusive passage of the original is given below, No. 20.

The other and much later passage which we have called *b*
has likewise already been referred to, and will be given more
fully in the original Italian. The speaker is not Galileo, but
'Salviati,' who to some extent represents Galileo, as 'Sagredo'
does also. For these two speakers in this dialogue of 1638 the
author took the actual names of two younger contemporaries,
Sagredo a Venetian and Salviati of Florence; the third
speaker, 'Simplicio,' is an Aristotelian man of straw who fares
ill in the argument, and whose name recalls the faithful sixth-
century commentator on the treatise *De Caelo*. According to
'Salviati,'

Aristotle says that 'an iron ball of one hundred pounds falling from
a height of one hundred cubits[49] reaches the ground before a one-pound
ball has fallen a single cubit.' I say that they arrive at the same time.
You find, on making the experiment, that the larger outstrips the
smaller by two finger-breadths, that is, when the larger has reached
the ground, the other is short of it by two finger-breadths; now you
would not hide behind these two fingers the ninety-nine cubits of
Aristotle.[50]

There we have the passage that has mainly led to the
unfounded modern talk about Aristotle's views on falling
bodies; it has been treated as if it were a verified citation from
Aristotle. I suggest that such is not the language, nor the
method, of experiment, but of a half-literary exercise, of a

[49] Galileo writes 'cento braccia'; the *braccio* differed in different Italian
cities, and even in measuring different goods. According to the *Enciclopedia
Italiana* (1928) the *braccio* at Florence = 0.584 of a metre; 100 *braccia*, then,
would be 58.4 metres. The same encyclopedia, in the ed. of 1884, gives the
height of the tower of Pisa as 54 metres.
[50] Galileo, *Dialogues concerning Two New Sciences*, trans. by Crew and De
Salvio, New York, 1914, pp. 64-5; see below, passage No. 25. The translators
use the quotation-marks, following the *Ed. Naz.* 8.109, which they say is es-
sentially the Elzevir ed. of 1638.

vernacular dialogue from seventeenth-century Italy.[51] What purports to be a direct quotation is a piece of expository imagination; and the likelihood that actual experiment is referred to is on a par with the sheer invention by Galileo of an utterance for Aristotle. The account by Viviani, written in 1654, was not published until 1717,[52] after which any one could join the story of the tower of Pisa with this speech of 'Salviati' (where no tower is mentioned), and the myth we have been studying more probably began to spread.

(3) It is commonly supposed that Aristotle never experimented, but simply observed natural phenomena. It is in general true that we have in his writings the results of his scientific method, rather than the processes. An attempt to infer the processes might well set him in a more favorable light nowadays, since our age stresses experiment, and honors the investigator who can and does supply conditions and apparatus so as to produce and study effects that would not occur without his interference. I do not here propose to array the evidence that Aristotle experimented in our sense, and merely note two cases in which it appears that he did so. The first is found in *Historia Animalium* 3.3.513[a]13-15; here he speaks of starving and then strangling animals, and it would

[51] Compare F. M. Denton of the University of New Mexico, *Why Wave Mechanics?* in *Scientific Monthly*, March, 1932, p. 197: 'If, for instance, he [Aristotle] had tried to picture a big and a little man throwing themselves simultaneously from the top of a tower,'[etc.] Galileo 'makes clear, without special experiment, the error of Aristotle's notion, who held that "an iron ball of one hundred pounds falling from a height of one hundred cubits reaches the ground before a one-pound ball has fallen a single cubit." ' Aristotle, thinks Denton, was an artist as well as a philosopher. Neither art nor science can suffer discontinuities. When blanks are found they must be filled—in art by fancy, in science by creation. Aristotle used fancy!

[52] In the *Fasti Consolari dell' Accademia Fiorentina* of Salvino Salvini, which appeared at Florence.

seem (*ibid.* 1.17.496^b4-6) that he had observed the effect of this procedure in the presence of blood in the heart and pulmonary vessels, and the absence of it in the lung proper. The other case is in *Physics* 4.8.216^a27-29: 'For as, if one puts a cube in water, an amount of water equal to the cube will be displaced; so too in air; but the effect is imperceptible to sense.' Soon after, *ibid.* 216^b2, we see that a cube of wood is meant. Aristotle's general scientific trend is shown by *De Gen. et Cor.* 2.316^a8-10 in his criticism: 'Those whom devotion to abstract discussions has rendered unobservant of the facts are too ready to generalize on the basis of a few observations.'

(4) And now we come to a rather cogent proof from Galileo himself that he did not while teaching at Pisa make the alleged experiment from the leaning tower.

But first I shall state the main argument of those scholars who hold that Viviani tells the truth about Galileo and the tower. They argue that Viviani, himself a respectable scientist, was in personal touch with Galileo in later years, as indeed he was, and hence that he must have heard from Galileo's own mouth an indubitable account of what happened at Pisa many years before. So Favaro, chief editor of the great National Edition of Galileo's works:

The fact of the experiments on the fall of heavy bodies, performed from the height of the tower of Pisa in order to demonstrate the new truths he had arrived at, is affirmed by Viviani, who must have had it from Galileo's own lips, [affirmed] in a manner so sure and explicit that it cannot be called into question, much less be flatly denied because no confirmation of it is found in contemporaneous documents.[53]

[53] Antonio Favaro, *Galileo Galilei*, Rome, third ed., 1922, p. 17; 'Il fatto delle esperienze sulla caduta dei gravi eseguite dall'alto della torre di Pisa,

That is not really argument. Why *'must'* have had it, from the *'very lips'* of Galileo? Viviani nowhere says that he so learnt it, but we have seen that he could have got the notion of 'experiments,' 'demonstrations,' and 'discourses,' from the treatise and the dialogue *De Motu*. Nor is he writing in our day of scholarly exactitude, when a serious author does tend to exclude marvels from biography. Instead, Viviani belongs to an age in which we must be prepared to find marvels of a biographical sort intermingled with scholarship or science that is otherwise competent and good for its day. In dealing with old writers, we have to reckon with their occasional wish to astound us, and must be on our guard against the human tendency to make things interesting by additions. Galileo himself is not incapable of straining a story to make it lively; and all of us are capable of mistaking illusion for reality in what we hear and see. The reader may even ask himself a question about the credibility of the following passage. It is the only one I know of in which Galileo seems to say clearly that he dropped objects of different weights from a tower. I beg the reader to attend with care to what is said, for I merely translate a passage, from the treatise *De Motu* (of about 1590), that would be contemporary with the alleged experiments which Favaro accepts on the word of Viviani; Galileo takes issue with Borri, his predecessor, on the reason why wood, as Galileo still thinks, in the beginning of its fall moves more quickly than lead:

If the large amount of air in wood made it go quicker, then as

per dimostrare le nuove verità alle quali era pervenuto, è dal Viviani, il quale deve averlo raccolto dalle labbra istesse di Galileo, affermato in modo così sicuro ed esplicito da non potersi revocarlo in dubbio, e tanto meno recisamente negare perchè non se ne trova conferma in altri documenti contemporanei.'

long as it is in the air the wood will move ever more quickly. But experience [or 'experiment'] shows the contrary; for, it is true, in the beginning of its motion the wood is carried more rapidly than the lead; but a little later the motion of the lead is so accelerated that it leaves the wood behind; and if they are let go from a high tower, precedes it by a long space; and I have often made test of this. So must we aim to draw the sounder reason from the sounder suppositions. O how readily are true demonstrations drawn from true principles![54]

There were currents and cross-currents of scientific opinion when Galileo was in his formative period, and he was played upon by various influences. It is not fair to say precisely that he steps out of one tradition into another, but that was approximately what he did. In his earliest studies he held with Aristotle; in *De Motu* we see him breaking with Aristotle, yet taking up with a new tradition. The passage we have just read from him cannot evince unbiased experiment, and doubtless would show an influence upon Galileo from his study of the tradition opposed to Aristotle; that is, it would still seem traditional if we could trace it to its sources in books that Galileo had been reading. And I now submit that in the other supposed experiment he mentions, in which two stones of differing masses should be flung 'from a high tower,'[55] he betrays either the influence of Benedetti[56] or some other

[54] Galileo, *De Motu*, Caput. . . . 'in which the reason is given why less heavy bodies in the beginning of their natural motion are carried more quickly than more heavy'; *Ed. Naz.* 1.333,334; see below, passage No. 23.

[55] *Ed. Naz.* 1. 263 (already quoted in translation, p. 50) : 'ex alta turri'; *cf.* 'ex turri' (1.273), 'ex sola turris altitudine' (1.329), 'ab alta turri' (1.406), 'ex altitudine turris' (1.407), 'unius turris' (*ibid.*), 'ex locis altissimis' (*ibid.*) There is not the slightest indication in these expressions, nor in their context, that Galileo has any nameable tower or height in mind.

[56] On Galileo and Benedetti, see G. Vailati in *Atti della R. Accademia delle Scienze di Torrino* 33 (1897-98). 359-83; G. Bordiga in *Atti del R. Istituto Veneto di Scienze, Lettere ed Arti* 85 (1925-6). 585-754.

intermediary, or else the influence of the Commentary to
which all the Italian writers go back on this question.[57] Galileo
mentions Philoponus early: in the *Tractatio prima de Mundo*,
Quaestio prima, *Ed. Naz.* 1.23, and in *De Motu* (in the
treatise and jottings), *Ed. Naz.* 1.284, 410. Viviani says that
Galileo learnt Greek as a youth;[58] and Philoponus'
commentary, ed. by Trincavelli, which was used by Benedetti
and many others in Greek or in the Latin translations, must
have been accessible to Galileo in more than one shape, thanks
to the activity of scholars who took part in the revival and
popularization of Greek science in the sixteenth century. In
fact, the rediscovery of Aristotle's 'error' about the relative
speed of falling bodies seems to run parallel with the
rediscovery of Aristarchus' heliocentric theory of the solar
system. It had to wait upon the discovery or development of
printing in Italy, upon the multiplication of books through
the printer's art, and, perhaps above all, upon the spread of
Latin translations of those Greek books in which the seeds of
modern physical science are contained. I have heard that there
still are rediscoveries to be made from Greek mathematics.

Now I proceed to our list of passages. When they come
from foreign languages, and have been sufficiently exploited

---

[57] Philoponus *In quattuor priores Libros Physicorum*, Venice, 1539; Latin
translation by Dorotheus, 1539, 1541; a better translation by Rasarius, Venice,
1558, 1559, 1581. In the treatise *De Motu* by Francesco Buonamici, pub. 1591, a
book which Galileo owned and cites, the author makes an interesting reference
to Philoponus 'and other Latin writers' who 'attacked Aristotle with the utmost
vigor with respect to the doctrine of thrown bodies, so that it can be said that
they have deserted the flag of their teacher.' I could not consult this work;
see Wohlwill in *Physikalische Zeitschrift* 7 (1906).24.

[58] Viviani, *Racconto* (*Ed. Naz.* 1.601): 'In questo tempo si diede ancora ad
apprendere la lingua greca, della quale fece acquisto non mediocre, conservan-
dola e servendosene poi opportunamente nelli studii più gravi.'

in the foregoing pages, I here give only the original text with a reference back; otherwise a translation accompanies the text. The passages are in a roughly chronological order; the apparent exception of Lucretius, who is placed at the beginning, is explained by the fact that the tradition of the Atomists, which he here represents, is anterior to Aristotle.

PASSAGES FOR REFERENCE AND ILLUSTRATION

(1) LUCRETIUS *De Rerum Natura* 2.230-9

Nam per aquas quaecumque cadunt atque aera rarum,
haec pro ponderibus casus celerare necessest
propterea quia corpus aquae naturaque tenuis
aeris haut possunt aeque rem quamque morari,
sed citius cedunt grauioribus exsuperata.
at contra nulli de nulla parte neque ullo
tempore inane potest uacuum subsistere rei,
quin, sua quod natura petit, concedere pergat;
omnia quapropter debent per inane quietum
aeque ponderibus non aequis concita ferri.[1]

[For the translation, see above, p. 49.]

(2) ARISTOTLE *De Caelo* 1.2.268^{b}20-4

Κύκλῳ μὲν οὖν ἐστὶν ἡ περὶ τὸ μέσον, εὐθεῖα δ' ἡ ἄνω καὶ κάτω. λέγω δ'
ἄνω μὲν τὴν ἀπὸ τοῦ μέσου, κάτω δὲ τὴν ἐπὶ τὸ μέσον. ὥστ' ἀνάγκη
πᾶσαν εἶναι τὴν ἁπλῆν φορὰν τὴν μὲν ἀπὸ τοῦ μέσου, τὴν δ' ἐπὶ τὸ μέσον,
τὴν δὲ περὶ τὸ μέσον.

---

[1] Pretty clearly, a predecessor, or predecessors, of Epicurus held a theory that would be known to Aristotle, since he was familiar with the views of the Atomists; the theory that objects of different size and weight would of their own motion move with equal swiftness in a 'void,' or, as we should now say, vacuum. Nausiphanes perhaps it was with whom we should associate the view that, in the 'void,' atoms of different weights move downwards with equal speeds. Nausiphanes, slightly senior to Epicurus, would fall within the period of Aristotle's activity. At all events the view in question was held by Epicurus, and hence reappears in the poem of Lucretius; cf. Cyril Bailey, *The Greek Atomists and Epicurus*, Oxford, 1928, pp. 129 f., 217-8, 311; Epicurus, Epistle 1.60-1; Lucretius 1.225 ff.; and Bailey in his edition of Epicurus, Oxford, 1926, p. 216. Cornford in Aristotle, *The Physics*, Loeb Classical Library, 1.357, says of 'this truth'—that a feather and a guinea will fall at the same pace through a vacuum—that it 'was divined, without experiment, by Epicurus.'

Now revolution about the centre is circular motion, while the upward and downward movements are in a straight line. 'Upward' means away from the centre, and 'downward' means motion towards the centre. All simple motion, then, must be motion either away from or towards or about the centre.[2]

(3) ARISTOTLE *De Caelo* 2.14.296ª31-2

Νῦν δ' ἐπ' εὐθείας πάντα φέρεται πρὸς τὸ μέσον.

In fact, every part moves in a straight line to the centre.

(4) ARISTOTLE *De Caelo* 2.13.294ª12-16

Τάχα γὰρ ἀλυποτέρας διανοίας τὸ μὴ θαυμάζειν πῶς ποτὲ μικρὸν μὲν μόριον τῆς γῆς, ἂν μετεωρισθὲν ἀφεθῇ, φέρεται καὶ μένειν οὐκ ἐθέλει, καὶ τὸ πλεῖον ἀεὶ θᾶττον, πᾶσαν δὲ τὴν γῆν εἴ τις ἀφείη μετεωρίσας, οὐκ ἂν φέροιτο.

[For the translation, see above, p. 38]

(5) ARISTOTLE *De Caelo* 2.13.294ᵇ3-6

Ἔτι δ' εἴπερ ὅλη πέφυκε μένειν ἐφ' ὕδατος, δῆλον ὅτι καὶ τῶν μορίων ἕκαστον· νῦν δ' οὐ φαίνεται τοῦτο γιγνόμενον, ἀλλὰ τὸ τυχὸν μόριον φέρεται εἰς βυθόν, καὶ θᾶττον τὸ μεῖζον.

Again, if the earth as a whole is capable of floating upon water, that must obviously be the case with any part of it. But observation shows that this is not the case. Any piece of earth goes to the bottom, the quicker the larger it is.[3]

---

[2] The English translation of passages from *De Caelo* is that of J. L. Stocks (1922) in *The Works of Aristotle*, translated into English, edited by W. D. Ross; the few changes I have introduced are of a minor sort.

[3] Aristotle argues against the view held by Thales of Miletus concerning the earth as a whole.

(6) ARISTOTLE *De Caelo* 3.2.301ᵃ20-ᵇ31

Ὅτι μὲν τοίνυν ἐστὶ φυσική τις κίνησις ἑκάστου τῶν σωμάτων, ἦν οὐ βίᾳ κινοῦνται οὐδὲ παρὰ φύσιν, φανερὸν ἐκ τούτων· ὅτι δ' ἔνια ἔχειν ἀναγκαῖον ῥοπὴν βάρους καὶ κουφότητος ἐκ τῶνδε δῆλον. κινεῖσθαι μὲν γὰρ φαμεν ἀναγκαῖον εἶναι· εἰ δὲ μὴ ἕξει φύσει ῥοπὴν τὸ κινούμενον, ἀδύνατον κινεῖσθαι ἢ πρὸς τὸ μέσον ἢ ἀπὸ τοῦ μέσου. ἔστω γὰρ τὸ μὲν ἐφ' οὗ Α ἀβαρές, τὸ δ' ἐφ' οὗ Β βάρος ἔχον, ἐνηνέχθω δὲ τὸ ἀβαρὲς τὴν ΓΔ, τὸ δὲ Β ἐν τῷ ἴσῳ χρόνῳ τὴν ΓΕ· μείζω γὰρ οἰσθήσεται τὸ βάρος ἔχον. ἐὰν δὴ διαιρεθῇ τὸ σῶμα τὸ ἔχον βάρος ὡς ἡ ΓΕ πρὸς τὴν ΓΔ (δυνατὸν γὰρ οὕτως ἔχειν πρός τι τῶν ἐν αὐτῷ μορίων), εἰ τὸ ὅλον φέρεται τὴν ὅλην τὴν ΓΕ, τὸ μόριον ἀνάγκη ἐν τῷ αὐτῷ χρόνῳ τὴν ΓΔ φέρεσθαι, ὥστε ἴσον οἰσθήσεται τὸ ἀβαρὲς καὶ τὸ βάρος ἔχον· ὅπερ ἀδύνατον. ὁ δ' αὐτὸς λόγος καὶ ἐπὶ κουφότητος. ἔτι δ' εἰ ἔσται τι σῶμα κινούμενον μήτε κουφότητα μήτε βάρος ἔχον, ἀνάγκη τοῦτο βίᾳ κινεῖσθαι, βίᾳ δὲ κινούμενον ἄπειρον ποιεῖν τὴν κίνησιν. ἐπεὶ γὰρ δύναμίς τις ἡ κινοῦσα, τὸ δ' ἔλαττον καὶ τὸ κουφότερον ὑπὸ τῆς αὐτῆς δυνάμεως πλεῖον κινηθήσεται, κεκινήσθω τὸ μὲν ἐφ' ᾧ τὸ Α, τὸ ἀβαρές, τὴν ΓΕ, τὸ δ' ἐφ' ᾧ τὸ Β, τὸ βάρος ἔχον, ἐν τῷ ἴσῳ χρόνῳ τὴν ΓΔ. διαιρεθέντος δὴ τοῦ βάρος ἔχοντος σώματος ὡς ἡ ΓΕ πρὸς τὴν ΓΔ, συμβήσεται τὸ ἀφαιρούμενον ἀπὸ τοῦ βάρος ἔχοντος σώματος τὴν ΓΕ φέρεσθαι ἐν τῷ ἴσῳ χρόνῳ, ἐπείπερ τὸ ὅλον ἐφέρετο τὴν ΓΔ. τὸ γὰρ τάχος ἕξει τὸ τοῦ ἐλάττονος πρὸς τὸ τοῦ μείζονος ὡς τὸ μεῖζον σῶμα πρὸς τὸ ἔλαττον. ἴσον ἄρα τὸ ἀβαρὲς οἰσθήσεται σῶμα καὶ τὸ βάρος ἔχον ἐν τῷ αὐτῷ χρόνῳ. τοῦτο δ' ἀδύνατον· ὥστ' ἐπεὶ παντὸς τοῦ προστεθέντος μεῖζον κινήσεται διάστημα τὸ ἀβαρές, ἄπειρον ἂν φέροιτο. φανερὸν οὖν ὅτι ἀνάγκη πᾶν σῶμα βάρος ἔχειν ἢ κουφότητα τὸ διωρισμένον. ἐπεὶ δὲ φύσις μέν ἐστιν ἡ ἐν αὐτῷ ὑπάρχουσα κινήσεως ἀρχή, δύναμις δ' ἡ ἐν ἄλλῳ ᾗ ἄλλο, κίνησις δὲ ἡ μὲν κατὰ φύσιν ἡ δὲ βίαιος πᾶσα, τὴν μὲν κατὰ φύσιν, οἷον τῷ λίθῳ τὴν κάτω, θᾶττον ποιήσει τὸ κατὰ δύναμιν, τὴν δὲ παρὰ φύσιν ὅλως αὐτή. πρὸς ἀμφότερα δὲ ὥσπερ ὀργάνῳ χρῆται τῷ ἀέρι· πέφυκε γὰρ οὗτος καὶ κοῦφος εἶναι καὶ βαρύς. τὴν μὲν οὖν ἄνω ποιήσει φορὰν ᾗ κοῦφος, ὅταν ὠσθῇ καὶ λάβῃ τὴν ἀρχὴν ἀπὸ τῆς δυνάμεως, τὴν δὲ κάτω πάλιν ᾗ βαρύς· ὥσπερ γὰρ ἐναφάψασα παραδίδωσιν ἑκατέρῳ. διὸ καὶ οὐ παρακολουθοῦντος τοῦ κινήσαντος φέρεται τὸ βίᾳ κινηθέν. εἰ γὰρ μὴ τοιοῦτόν τι τὸ σῶμα ὑπῆρχεν, οὐκ ἂν ἦν ἡ βία κίνησις. καὶ τὴν κατὰ φύσιν δ' ἑκάστου κίνησιν συνεπουρίζει τὸν αὐτὸν τρόπον. ὅτι μὲν οὖν ἅπαν ἢ κοῦφον ἢ βαρύ, καὶ πῶς αἱ παρὰ φύσιν ἔχουσι κινήσεις, ἐκ τούτων φανερόν.

These [*i.e.*, the foregoing] arguments make it plain that every body has its natural movement, which is not constrained or contrary to its nature. We go on to show that there are certain bodies whose necessary impetus is that of weight and lightness. Of necessity, we assert, they must move, and a moved thing which has no natural impetus cannot move either towards or away from the centre. Suppose a body A without weight, and a body B endowed with weight. Suppose the weightless body to move the distance CD, while B in the same time moves the distance CE, which will be greater since the heavy thing must move further. Let the heavy body then be divided in the proportion CE : CD (for there is no reason why a part of B should not stand in this relation to the whole). Now if the whole moves the whole distance CE, the part must in the same time move the distance CD. A weightless body, therefore, and one which has weight will move the same distance, which is impossible. And the same argument would fit the case of lightness. Again, a body which is in motion, but has neither weight nor lightness, must be moved by constraint, and must continue its constrained movement infinitely. For there will be a force which moves it, and the smaller and lighter a body is the further will a given force move it. Now let A, the weightless body, be moved the distance CE, and B, which has weight, be moved in the same time the distance CD. Dividing the heavy body in the proportion CE : CD, we subtract from the heavy body a part which will in the same time move the distance CE, since the whole moved CD, for the relative speeds of the two bodies will be in inverse ratio to their respective sizes. Thus the weightless body will move the same distance as the heavy in the same time. But this is impossible. Hence, since the motion of the weightless body will cover a greater distance than any that is suggested, it will continue infinitely. It is therefore obvious that every body must have a definite weight or lightness. But since 'nature' means a source of movement within the thing itself, while a force is a source of movement in something other than it or in itself *quâ* other, and since movement is always due either to nature or to constraint, movement which is natural, as downward movement is to a stone, will be merely accelerated by an external force, while an unnatural movement will be due to the force alone. In either case the air is as it were instrumental to the force. For air is both light and heavy, and thus *quâ* light produces upward motion, being propelled and set in motion by the force, and *quâ* heavy produces a downward motion. In either case the force transmits the movement to the body by first, as it were, impregnating the air. That is why a body moved by constraint continues to move when that which gave the impulse ceases to accompany it. Otherwise, *i.e.*, if the air were not endowed with this function, constrained movement would be impossible. And the natural movement of a body may be helped on in the same way. This discussion suffices to show (1) that all bodies are either light or heavy, and (2) how unnatural movement takes place.

(7) ARISTOTLE *De Caelo* 4.2.309ª27-ᵇ18

Ἀναγκαῖον δὲ καὶ τοῖς περὶ τῆς τοῦ πυρὸς κουφότητος αἰτιωμένοις τὸ πολὺ κενὸν ἔχειν σχεδὸν ἐν ταῖς αὐταῖς ἐνέχεσθαι δυσχερείαις. ἔλαττον μὲν γὰρ ἕξει στερεὸν τῶν ἄλλων σωμάτων, καὶ τὸ κενὸν πλεῖον· ἀλλ' ὅμως ἔσται τι κυρὸς πλῆθος ἐν ᾧ τό στερεὸν καὶ τὸ πλῆρες ὑπερβάλλει τῶν περιεχομένων στερεῶν ἔν τινι μικρῷ πλήθει γῆς. ἐὰν δὲ φῶσι καὶ τὸ κενόν, πῶς διοριοῦσι τὸ ἁπλῶς βαρύ; ἢ γὰρ τῷ πλεῖον στερεὸν ἔχειν ἢ τῷ ἔλαττον κενόν. εἰ μὲν οὖν τοῦτο φήσουσιν, ἔσται τι πλῆθος γῆς οὕτως ὀλίγον ἐν ᾧ στερεὸν ἔσται ἔλαττον ἢ ἐν πολλῷ πλήθει πυρός. ὁμοίως δὲ κἂν τῷ κενῷ διορίσωσιν, ἔσται τι κουφότερον τοῦ ἁπλῶς κούφου καὶ φερομένου ἀεὶ ἄνω αὐτὸ φερόμενον ἀεὶ κάτω. τοῦτο δὲ ἀδύνατον· τὸ γὰρ ἁπλῶς κοῦφον ἀεὶ κουφότερον τῶν ἐχόντων βάρος καὶ κάτω φερομένων, τὸ δὲ κουφότερον οὐκ ἀεὶ κοῦφον διὰ τὸ λέγεσθαι καὶ ἐν τοῖς ἔχουσι βάρος ἕτερον ἑτέρου κουφότερον, οἷον γῆς ὕδωρ. ἀλλὰ μὴν οὐδὲ τῷ τὸ κενὸν ἀνάλογον ἔχειν πρὸς τὸ πλῆρες ἱκανὸν λῦσαι τὴν λεγομένην νῦν ἀπορίαν. συμβήσεται γὰρ καὶ τοῦτον τὸν τρόπον λέγουσιν ὡσαύτως τὸ ἀδύνατον. ἐν γὰρ τῷ πλείονι πυρὶ καὶ ἐν τῷ ἐλάττονι τὸν αὐτὸν ἕξει λόγον τὸ στερεὸν πρὸς τὸ κενόν. φέρεται δέ γε θᾶττον τὸ πλεῖον ἄνω πῦρ τοῦ ἐλάττονος, καὶ κάτω δὲ πάλιν ὡσαύτως ὁ πλείων χρυσὸς καὶ ὁ μόλιβδος· ὁμοίως δὲ καὶ τῶν ἄλλων ἕκαστον τῶν ἐχόντων βάρος. οὐκ ἔδει δὲ τοῦτο συμβαίνειν, εἴπερ τούτῳ διώρισται τὸ βαρὺ καὶ κοῦφον. ἄτοπον δὲ καὶ εἰ διὰ τὸ κενὸν μὲν ἄνω φέρονται, τὸ δὲ κενὸν αὐτὸ μή.

But those who attribute the lightness of fire to its containing so much void are necessarily involved in practically the same difficulties. For though fire be supposed to contain less solid than any other body, as well as more void, yet there will be a certain quantum of fire in which the amount of solid or plenum is in excess of the solids contained in some small quantity of earth. They may reply that there is an excess of void also. But the question is, how will they discriminate the absolutely heavy? Presumably, either by its excess of solid or by its defect of void. On the former view there could be an amount of earth so small as to contain less solid than a large mass of fire. And, similarly, if the distinction rests on the amount of void, there will be a body, lighter than the absolutely light, which nevertheless moves downward as constantly as the other moves upward. But that cannot be so, since the absolutely light is always lighter than bodies which have weight and move downward, while, on the other hand, that which is lighter need not be light, because in common speech we distinguish a lighter and a heavier (viz. water and earth) among bodies endowed with weight. Again, the suggestion of a certain ratio between the void and the solid in a body is no more equal to solving the problem before us. This manner of speaking will issue in a similar impossibility. For any two portions of fire, small or great, will exhibit the same ratio of solid to void; but the upward movement of the greater is quicker than that of the less, just as the downward movement of a mass of gold or lead, or of any other body endowed with weight, is quicker in proportion to its size. This, however, should not be the case if the ratio is the ground of distinction between heavy things and light. There is also an absurdity in attributing the upward movement of bodies to a void which does not itself move.

(8) ARISTOTLE *De Caelo* 4.2.308^{b}13-28

Νῦν γὰρ τὸ μὲν πῦρ ἀεὶ κοῦφον καὶ ἄνω φέρεται, ἡ δὲ γῆ καὶ τὰ γεηρὰ πάντα κάτω καὶ πρὸς τὸ μέσον. ὥστ᾽ οὐ δι᾽ ὀλιγότητα τῶν τριγώνων ἐξ ὧν συνεστάναι φασὶν ἕκαστον αὐτῶν, τὸ πῦρ ἄνω φέρεσθαι πέφυκεν· τό τε γὰρ πλεῖον ἧττον ἂν ἐφέρετο καὶ βαρύτερον ἂν ἦν ἐκ πλειόνων ὂν τριγώνων. νῦν δὲ φαίνεται τοὐναντίον· ὅσῳ γὰρ ἂν ᾖ πλεῖον, κουφότερόν ἐστι καὶ ἄνω φέρεται θᾶττον. καὶ ἄνωθεν δὲ κάτω τὸ ὀλίγον οἰσθήσεται θᾶττον πῦρ, τὸ δὲ πολὺ βραδύτερον. πρὸς δὲ τούτοις, ἐπεὶ τὸ μὲν ἐλάσσω ἔχον τὰ ὁμογενῆ κουφότερον εἶναί φασι, τὸ δὲ πλείω βαρύτερον, ἀέρα δὲ καὶ ὕδωρ καὶ πῦρ ἐκ τῶν αὐτῶν εἶναι τριγώνων, ἀλλὰ διαφέρειν ὀλιγότητι καὶ πλήθει, διὸ τὸ μὲν αὐτῶν εἶναι κουφότερον τὸ δὲ βαρύτερον, ἔσται τι πλῆθος ἀέρος ὃ βαρύτερον ὕδατος ἔσται. συμβαίνει δὲ πᾶν τοὐναντίον· ἀεί τε γὰρ ὁ πλείων ἀὴρ ἄνω φέρεται μᾶλλον, καὶ ὅλως ὁτιοῦν μέρος ἀέρος ἄνω φέρεται ἐκ τοῦ ὕδατος.

The facts are that fire is always light and moves upward, while earth and all earthy things move downwards or towards the centre. . . . The palpable fact . . . is that the greater the quantity, the lighter the mass is, and the quicker its upward movement; and, similarly, in the reverse movement from above downward, the small mass will move quicker and the large slower. Further, since to be lighter is to have fewer of these homogeneous parts and to be heavier is to have more, and air, water, and fire are composed of the same triangles [according to the argument Aristotle here combats], the only difference being in the number of such parts, which must therefore explain any distinction of relatively light and heavy between these bodies, it follows that there must be a certain quantum of air which is heavier than water. But the facts are entirely opposed to this. The larger the quantity of air the more readily it moves upward, and any portion of air without exception will rise out of water.

(9) ARISTOTLE *De Caelo* 4.4.311ᵃ16-27

Πρῶτον μὲν οὖν διωρίσθω, καθάπερ φαίνεται πᾶσι, βαρὺ μὲν ἁπλῶς τὸ πᾶσιν ὑφιστάμενον, κοῦφον δὲ τὸ πᾶσιν ἐπιπολάζον. ἁπλῶς δὲ λέγω εἴς τε τὸ γένος βλέπων, καὶ ὅσοις μὴ ἀμφότερα ὑπάρχει· οἷον φαίνεται πυρὸς μὲν τὸ τυχὸν μέγεθος ἄνω φερόμενον, ἐὰν μή τι τύχῃ κωλῦον ἕτερον, γῆς δὲ κάτω· τὸν αὐτὸν δὲ τρόπον καὶ θᾶττον τὸ πλεῖον. ἄλλως δὲ βαρὺ καὶ κοῦφον, οἷς ἀμφότερα ὑπάρχει· καὶ γὰρ ἐπιπολάζουσί τισι καὶ ὑφίσταν- ται, καθάπερ ἀὴρ καὶ ὕδωρ· ἁπλῶς μὲν γὰρ οὐδέτερον τούτων κοῦφον ἢ βαρύ· γῆς μὲν γὰρ ἄμφω κουφότερα (ἐπιπολάζει γὰρ αὐτῇ τὸ τυχὸν αὐτῶν μόριον), πυρὸς δὲ βαρύτερα (ὑφίσταται γὰρ αὐτῶν ὁπόσον ἂν ᾖ μόριον).

In accordance with general conviction we may distinguish the absolutely heavy, as that which sinks to the bottom of all things, from the absolutely light, which is that which rises to the surface of all things. I use the term 'absolutely,' in view of the generic character of 'light' and 'heavy,' in order to confine the application to bodies which do not combine lightness and heaviness. It is apparent, I mean, that fire, in whatever quantity, so long as there is no external obstacle, moves upward, and earth downward; and, if the quantity is increased, the movement is the same, though swifter. But the heaviness and lightness of bodies which combine these qualities is different from this, since while they rise to the surface of some bodies they sink to the bottom of others. Such are air and water. Neither of them is absolutely either light or heavy. Both are lighter than earth—for any portion of either rises to the surface of it—but heavier than fire, since a portion of either, whatever its quantity, sinks to the bottom of fire.

(10) ARISTOTLE, *Physica* 4.8.214^{b}12-24

Ὅτι δ' οὐκ ἔστι κενὸν οὕτω κεχωρισμένον, ὡς ἔνιοί φασι, λέγωμεν πάλιν. εἰ γάρ ἐστιν ἑκάστου φορά τις τῶν ἁπλῶν σωμάτων φύσει, οἷον τῷ πυρὶ μὲν ἄνω τῇ δὲ γῇ κάτω καὶ πρὸς τὸ μέσον, δῆλον ὅτι οὐκ ἂν τὸ κενὸν αἴτιον εἴη τῆς φορᾶς. τίνος οὖν αἴτιον ἔσται τὸ κενόν; δοκεῖ γὰρ αἴτιον εἶναι κινήσεως τῆς κατὰ τόπον, ταύτης δ' οὐκ ἔστιν.

Ἔτι εἰ ἔστι τι οἷον τόπος ἐστερημένος σώματος, ὅταν ᾖ κενόν, ποῦ οἰσθήσεται τὸ εἰστεθὲν εἰς αὐτὸ σῶμα; οὐ γὰρ δὴ εἰς ἅπαν. ὁ δ' αὐτὸς λόγος καὶ πρὸς τοὺς τὸν τόπον οἰομένους εἶναί τι κεχωρισμένον, εἰς ὃν φέρεται· πῶς γὰρ οἰσθήσεται τὸ ἐντεθὲν ἢ μενεῖ; καὶ περὶ τοῦ ἄνω καὶ κάτω καὶ περὶ τοῦ κενοῦ ὁ αὐτὸς ἁρμόσει λόγος εἰκότως· τὸ γὰρ κενὸν τόπον ποιοῦσιν οἱ εἶναι φάσκοντες.

Let us explain again that there is no void existing separately, as some maintain. If each of the simple bodies has a natural locomotion, e.g., fire upward and earth downward and towards the middle of the universe, it is clear that it cannot be the void that is the condition of locomotion. What, then, *will* the void be the condition of? It is thought to be the condition of movement in respect of place, and it is not the condition of this.

Again, if void is a sort of place deprived of body, when there is a void where will a body placed in it move to? It certainly cannot move into the whole of the void. The same argument applies as against those who think that place is something separate, into which things are carried, viz.: how will what is placed in it move, or rest? Much the same argument will apply to the void as to the 'up' and 'down' in place, as is natural enough since those who maintain the existence of the void make it a place.[4]

(11) ARISTOTLE *Physica* 4.8.215ᵃ25-31

'Ορῶμεν γὰρ τὸ αὐτὸ βάρος καὶ σῶμα θᾶττον φερόμενον διὰ δύο αἰτίας, ἢ τῷ διαφέρειν τὸ δι' οὗ, οἷον δι' ὕδατος ἢ γῆς ἢ ἀέρος, ἢ τῷ διαφέρειν τὸ φερόμενον, ἐὰν τἆλλα ταὐτὰ ὑπάρχῃ, διὰ τὴν ὑπεροχὴν τοῦ βάρους ἢ τῆς κουφότητος.

Τὸ μὲν οὖν δι' οὗ φέρεται αἴτιον, ὅτι ἐμποδίζει μάλιστα μὲν ἀντιφερόμενον, ἔπειτα καὶ μένον· μᾶλλον δὲ τὸ μὴ εὐδιαίρετον· τοιοῦτο δὲ τὸ παχύτερον.

We see the same weight or body moving faster than another for two reasons, either because there is a difference in what it moves through, as between water, air, and earth, or because, other things being equal, the moving body differs from the other owing to excess of weight or of lightness.

[4] This and the following passage are given in the translation by Hardie and Gaye (1930) in *The Works of Aristotle*, translated into English, edited by W. D. Ross.

Now the medium causes a difference because it impedes the moving thing, most of all if it is moving in the opposite direction, but in a secondary degree even if it is at rest; and especially a medium that is not easily divided, *i.e.*, a medium that is somewhat dense.

(12) ARISTOTLE *Physica* 4.8.216ᵃ8-21

'Ως δ' ἐν κεφαλαίῳ εἰπεῖν, δῆλον τὸ τοῦ συμβαίνοντος αἴτιον, ὅτι κινήσεως μὲν πρὸς κίνησιν πάσης ἐστὶ λόγος (ἐν χρόνῳ γάρ ἐστι, χρόνου δὲ παντός ἐστι πρὸς χρόνον, πεπερασμένων ἀμφοῖν), κενοῦ δὲ πρὸς πλῆρες οὐκ ἔστιν.

*Ἡ μὲν οὖν διαφέρουσι δι' ὧν φέρονται, ταῦτα συμβαίνει, κατὰ δὲ τὴν τῶν φερομένων ὑπεροχὴν τάδε· ὁρῶμεν γὰρ τὰ μείζω ῥοπὴν ἔχοντα ἢ βάρους ἢ κουφότητος, ἐὰν τἆλλα ὁμοίως ἔχῃ τοῖς σχήμασι, θᾶττον φερόμενα τὸ ἴσον χωρίον, καὶ κατὰ λόγον ὃν ἔχουσι τὰ μεγέθη πρὸς ἄλληλα. ὥστε καὶ διὰ τοῦ κενοῦ. ἀλλ' ἀδύνατον· διὰ τίνα γὰρ αἰτίαν οἰσθήσεται θᾶττον; (ἐν μὲν γὰρ τοῖς πλήρεσιν ἐξ ἀνάγκης· θᾶττον γὰρ διαιρεῖ τῇ ἰσχύϊ τὸ μεῖζον· ἢ γὰρ σχήματι διαιρεῖ, ἢ ῥοπῇ ἣν ἔχει τὸ φερόμενον ἢ τὸ ἀφεθέν.) ἰσοταχῆ ἄρα πάντ' ἔσται. ἀλλ' ἀδύνατον.

[For the translation, see above, p. 40]

(13) PHILOPONUS, Commentary on Aristotle's *Physica*, Corollary on the Void (about A.D. 533), ed. Vitelli, p. 683

Τοῦτο δὲ παντελῶς ἐστι ψεῦδος. καὶ τοῦτο ἔστι πιστώσασθαι κρεῖττον πάσης διὰ λόγων ἀποδείξεως ἐξ αὐτῆς τῆς ἐναργείας. πολλῷ γὰρ πάνυ μέτρῳ διαφέροντα ἀλλήλων δύο βάρη ἅμα ἀφεὶς ἐκ τοῦ αὐτοῦ ὕψους ὄψει ὅτι οὐχ ἕπεται τῇ ἀναλογίᾳ τῶν βαρῶν ἡ ἀναλογία τοῦ χρόνου τῶν κινήσεων, ἀλλὰ πάνυ ἐλαχίστη τις ἡ διαφορὰ κατὰ τοὺς χρόνους γίνεται, ὡς εἰ μὴ πολλῷ πάνυ μέτρῳ διαφέροιεν ἀλλήλων τὰ βάρη, ἀλλ' οἷον τὸ μὲν διπλά- σιον εἴη τὸ δὲ ἥμισυ, οὐδὲ διαφοράν τινα σχήσουσιν οἱ χρόνοι τῶν κινήσεων, ἤ, εἰ καὶ σχήσουσιν, οὐκ αἰσθητὴν ἕξουσι.

[For the translation, see above, p. 47]

(14) DIAGRAM IN SIMPLICIUS' COMMENTARY ON ARISTOTLE *De Caelo* 3.2.301ᵃ22 (second quarter of the sixth century), ed. Heiberg, p. 592

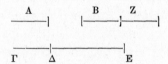

(15) LEONARDO DA VINCI (1452-1519), Codex Atlanticus, fol. 97 v a⁵

Vedi Aristotile de cielo e mondo.

See Aristotle *De Caelo*.

(16) LEONARDO DA VINCI, *Codex Atlanticus,* fol. 123 r a

Ogni (*Il*) grave quanto po da lieve si remove, (*e 'l suo* (*m*) *moto al centro del mondo si diriza*) e 'l suo centro nel centro delli elementi si quieta; al qual libero cadendo, per la via più brieve si diriza, e quant' è più (*d gra piu*) grave, più presto discende, e quanto più discende, più si fa veloce, e quanto il discenso è più obliquo, tanto il peso manca della sua gravezza, e mancando della sua gravezza, esso carica il suo sostentaculo. . . .

(*Sì come la levità (dell' elemento) del foco non è di tal forza che sostener possa gravezza dell' aria e similme*)

Sì come il foco è il più lieve elemento, così è di manco resistenzia; e se possibile fussi a condurre alla sua somma altezza (*di quello*) qualche quantità d'aria (*e*), essa aria per-

---

⁵ *Il Codice Atlantico di Leonardo da Vinci nella Biblioteca Ambrosiana di Milano* riprodotto e pubblicato dalla Regia Accademia dei Lincei, Milan, 1894.

forerebbe tale elemento, sanza mai dare riposo al suo discenso, fin che alla sua spera fussi condotta. Similmente, essendo l'aria di più levità che l'acqua, e già essa aria è di manco resistenzia; onde quando l'acqua, che lassù vapora, si riduce alla sua semplice natura, di là si discende, perforando (*essa*) l'aria, che sotto (*l*) (*che sotto*) non le po resistere, e al suo elemen[to] per la più bre[ve] via si conduce. Similmente la terra, più (*brie*) grave che l'acqua, se sarà posto alla (*sommità di*) superfizie d'essa acqua, quella, come più leggieri, non le potrà resistere, onde essa terra, per la più brieve via, al fondo dell'acqua si conduce. E se tutto questa spera della terra fussi acqua o aria, vedere essa gravità.

Dice Aristotile che ogni cosa desidera mantenere la sua natura.

La gravità, per essere rescacciata dalle cose lievi, desidera tal sito, che (*p*) essa più non pesi, che la sua densità rimanga senza peso, il qual trovato, più non pesa e più (*non*) per sè non si move.

La gravi(*za*)tà e la forza desidera non essere, e però (*l'una*) ciascuno con violenza (*si*) mantiene suo essere.

La cosa smossa desidera seguire la linia principiata dal suo motore.

La gravità, figliola del moto, sì come la forza, disidera disfarsi; e però ciascun con violenza mantien suo essere. E se possibil fussi dare un diamitro d'aria a questa spera della terra, a similitudine d' un pozzo che dall' una all' altra superfizie si mostrassi, e per esso pozzo (*si lasc*) si lasciassi cadere (*la pietra*) un corpo grave, ancora che esso corpo si volessi al centro fermare, l'impeto sarebbe quello che per molti anni glielo vieterebbe.

Every heavy body as much as it can removes itself from what is light, (*and its motion directs itself to the centre of the world*) and its centre is at rest in the centre of the elements; toward which, falling freely, it directs itself by the shortest path, and the heavier it is the sooner it descends, and the farther it descends the faster it goes, and the more oblique the descent the more the weight lacks gravity, and lacking its gravity it burdens what sustains it. . . .

(As the lightness (of the element) of fire is not of such force that it can sustain the weight of air and the like).

Just as fire is the lightest element, so is it wanting in resistance; and were it possible to conduct to the highest altitude (*of it*) some quantity of air, the air would go through such element, without ever giving repose to its descent, until it was conducted to its sphere. Similarly, air being of greater lightness than water, and air already wants resistance; hence when the water, which vaporizes up there, is reduced to its simple nature, it descends from there, going through the air, which beneath cannot resist it, and betakes itself by the shortest path to its element. Similarly earth, heavier than water, if placed at the surface of the water; this latter since it is more light cannot resist it, and the earth betakes itself by the shortest path to the bottom of the water. And if all this sphere of earth were water or air, [? some word omitted by Leonardo] see the gravity.

Aristotle says that everything desires to maintain its own nature.

Gravity, in order to be expelled from light things, desires such a position that it shall no longer have weight, that its density shall remain without weight; which position being found, it no longer has weight, and no longer is moved through itself.

Gravity and force desire not to be, and yet each with violence maintains its being.

A body in motion desires to follow the primary line of its mover.

Gravity, daughter of motion, desires, like force, to undo itself; and yet each with violence maintains its being. And were it possible to form a diameter of air for this sphere of earth, after the fashion of a well which should appear from one surface to the other, and if through this well you should let fall (*the stone*) a heavy body, still though you wished the body to settle at the centre the impetus would be such as to prevent it for many years.

(17) IVOR B. HART *The Mechanical Investigations of Leonardo da Vinci*, Chicago, 1925, pp. 56-8

[Hart probably is right in his view, though he wrongly ascribes the *Mechanica* to Aristotle. With the *Mechanica* in mind, Hart says:]

Aristotle . . . plays a great part in the building up of da Vinci's outlook. Direct references abound in his [da Vinci's] manuscripts. From the point of view of mechanics, we may regard Aristotle's work as the starting-point of a chain of thought which played an important part in the evolution of the subject up to the days of Leonardo da Vinci. Aristotle made no distinction between a theory of equilibrium and a theory of movement. That was a development which came after him. His standpoint was that of treating generally of mechanisms from the point of view of the movements which are produced in them. When in fact there are no such movements, he regarded the mechanism as being in equilibrium. What Aristotle called the 'motive power' which moves a body he measured by the product of the weight moved and its velocity. Aristotle used the term 'weight' very generally where we use the term 'mass.' There was no distinction between the two.

It followed from this conception of motive power that the same power would move a heavy body slowly, and a light body quickly, the velocities produced being, for the same power, inversely proportional to the weights. This principle, generally applicable to all mechanisms, he applied to the lever ... by showing that whilst the large mass M moved a distance x, m [the small mass] moved through X. Aristotle deduces that 'the weight which is moved is to the weight which moves in the inverse ratio of the lengths of the arms of the lever; always, in fact, a weight will move as much more easily as it is further from the fulcrum.' [Cf. *Mechanica* 3.850ª39-ᵇ3.] This sums up Aristotle's most important contribution to the history of mechanics. Duhem [*Origine de la Statique*, Paris, 1905, I.8] regards it, indeed, as 'la graine d'où sortiront par un developpement vingt fois seculaire les puissantes ramifications du Principe des vitesses virtuelles.' Aristotle's influence upon Leonardo is shown clearly in the following pronouncement:

[First:] if a force moves a body for a given time over a given distance, the same force will move half the mass in the same time through twice the distance.

Secondly: or again the same force will move half this mass through the same distance in half this time.

Thirdly: and half this force will move half the body through the same distance in the same time.

Fourthly: and this force will move twice the mass through the same distance in twice the time; and one thousand times the mass in one thousand times the time, through the same distance.

Fifthly: and the half of this force will move the whole of this mass through half the distance in the same time, and one hundred times the mass through one hundredth of the distance in the same time.

Sixthly: and if two separate forces move two separate bodies in so much time through so much distance, the same forces together would move the same bodies together all this distance in the same time, because the original proportions always remain the same. [*Cf.* Leonardo, MS. F., fol. 126 r.]

(18) JEROME CARDAN (1501?-1576), *Opus Novum de Proportionibus*, Basel, [1570], pp. 104-5, Lib. 5, Propositio centesimadecima

Si duae sphaerae ex eadem materia descendant in aëre eodem temporis momento ad planum ueniunt.

Supponitur quod ex eodem loco. Sermo enim absurda sub interpretatione nunquam nisi ab inuidioso, uel imperito intelligi debet. Sit ergo *a* tripla ad *b*, sphaerula ad sphaerulam ex plumbo ambae ferro uel lapide eiusdem generis, dico quod in aequali tempore peruenient ad planum *cd*. Nam *a* proportionem habet ad *b*, ut uigintiseptem ad unum; proportio autem spatii *a* ad spatium *b* nonupla est, et proportio densitatis aëris ad aërem est tripla, propterea quod densitas illa multiplicatur propter impetus magnitudinem; nam si robur, ut decem percutiat baculo lato, ut quattuor ictus erit maior duplo, quam sit robur, ut quinque percutiat baculo, ut duo: propter densitatem ergo maiorem aëris in *a* quam in *b*: et quoniam si sub maiore impetu mouetur aër sub *a*, quam sub *b*, igitur proportio erit comparanda longitudini a centro *a* ad longitudinem a centro *b*, quae est tripla. Si ergo subtripla est ratio motus *b* ad *a*, quod ad medium attinet, tripla autem propter uelocitatem discessus aëris a medio grauitatis, quod est in superficie e regione centri gravitatis in linea ad centrum mundi, ut dictum est in praecedenti: manifestum est, quod *a*, et *b* in aequali tempore peruenient ad subiectum planum, et aequidistans centris eorum. Similiter et in aqua: [Cardan, p. 105] cum uero uideatur in illa tanto celerius *a* descendere, quam *b*, quanto est semidiameter *a* longior semidiametro *b*, liquet ex hoc, quod aequali uelocitate descendunt, sed ob uelocitatem motus in aëre latet discrimen anticipationis contactus soli *a* ante *b*, qui dignoscitur in aqua, ex quo patet exactam esse aequalitatem. Sed resiliunt semel in aqua ambae, cum pluries in aëre a solo, quare etiam in aqua perturbatur cognitio in parum accuratis, atque sensu praeditis, sicut etiam in casu; ne altera alteram perueniat, utraque comprehensa duobus digitis, altera alteram tangente, et usque ad centrum in aquam demissis simul digitis dilatatis dimittendae sunt.

A New Work on Proportions, Book 5, Proposition 110

Two balls of the same material falling in air arrive at a plane at the same instant.

It is assumed that they fall from the same point; for a proposition is not to be taken in an absurd sense unless by an invidious or ignorant critic. Let *a*, therefore, be triple the size of *b*, two balls alike of lead, iron, or stone of a given sort. I say that they will reach the plane *cd* in equal times. For *a* has the [cubic] proportion to *b* of 27 to 1; but [for the surfaces] the spatial proportion of *a* to *b* is 9 to 1; and the proportion of the density of air to air [the pressure on air of *a* as compared with *b*] is 3 to 1, because that density [resistant pressure] must be mutiplied on account of the impetus [of *a*]. For example, if the force needed to make a broad staff strike 10 as compared with the force needed to make it strike 5 is as 4 blows to 2, so will the case be on account of the greater density [resistant pressure] of air upon *a* as compared with *b*. So also since, if the air is moved under the greater impetus under *a* than under *b*, the proportion must be got by comparing the length [of the radius] from the centre of *a* to that from the centre of *b*, namely 3 to 1. If, therefore, the ratio of the motion of *b* to that of *a* is 1 to 3 so far as concerns the middle [the diameters], but is 3 to 1 because of the speed of the departing of the air from the centre of gravity, that is, as aforesaid, superficially in a straight line from the centre of gravity to the centre of the world; then it is manifest that *a* and *b* will arrive at the plane below in equal times and at an equal distance from their centres.

The same thing holds in water. Though in water, it is true, *a* seems to go down quicker than *b* [in proportion] as the radius of *a* is longer than the radius of *b*, yet it results from this that they go down with equal velocity; but, because of the rapidity of motion in air, our judgment of anticipation, that *a*

makes contact with the ground before *b*, escapes detection;
but the fact is recognized in water, whence it is plain that the
equality is exact. But both balls give one bounce in water, as
in air they give several from the ground, and hence in water
also perception is disturbed for less accurate persons, even
those endowed with better senses, just as in the case of fall. In
order that one ball may not meet the other, each should be
held in two fingers, one ball touching the other, and the
fingers letting the ball down to the centre into the water, and
then with the fingers simultaneously spread both balls should
be let go.

(19) SIMON STEVIN (1548-1620)

*Liber Primus Staticae de Staticae Elementis. Statices Liber
Secundus qui est de Inveniendo Gravitatis Centro. De Staticae
Principiis Liber Tertius de Staticae Praxi. Liber Quartus
Staticae de Hydrostatices Elementis. Appendix Statices . . .*
Caput II. Res motas impedimentis suis non esse propor-
tionales. Leyden, 1605, p. 151.

In Praxis Statices ad Lectorem praefatione diximus res
motas suis impedimentis non esse proportionales, ejusque
demonstrationi hunc locum destinavimus, ut argumenta aliter
sentientium refutemus. Principio Aristoteles ejusque sectatores
4 Physic. cap. de inani existimat corporibus duobus similibus
et materia aequipondiis per aërem delapsis eandem esse
rationem ponderis ad pondus quae velocitatis illius ad
velocitatem hujus, id est quae sit impedimenti ad im-
pedimentum. Quam sententiam variis locis clarius proponit,
ut 6 Physic. item 1, 2, 3, 4 de Coelo, aliisque compluribus;
sententiam hanc Ioannes Taisnerus Hannonius oppugnavit,

proportionem quidem hactenus admittens ut corpora ista aequali temporis spatio aequalia permeent intervalla. Cui opinioni Cardanus lib. 5 Proportion. propos. 110 consentit. Sed utrosque hallucinari ipsa experientia demonstrabimus, ac deinde ejus causam declarabimus. Experientia vero contra Aristotelem istiusmodi est; sumito duos plumbeos globos (quod Cl. vir Ioannes Grotius, sedulus naturae indagator, et ego quondam experti sumus) ponderis ratione decupla, eos altitudine 30 pedum pariter demittito in subjectum asserem, aliudve solidum unde sonus clare reddatur; manifeste cognosces leviorem non decuplo tardius graviore, sed pariter in asserem incidere ut sonitus utriusque illisu redditus unus idemque videatur. Idemque contingit in corporibus magnitudinis aequalis, gravitatis vero decuplae: Quare dicta ista Aristotelis proportio a vero aliena est. Sed alterum experimentum hujusmodi contra Taisnerum facit: Sumito e gossipio lanave tenue quoddam et exile filum atque sarcinulam ex eadem materia pondere unius librae dense firmiterque colligatam, et forma filo simili, hęc pariter quinque aut sex pedum altitudine dimittito, re ipsa cognosces filum longe diutius in aëre morari, quam sarcinulam etsi fili materia longe compactior densiorque sit sarcinula quae multum aëris admittit. Quare aequale spacium ab ipsis pari velocitate non transitur.[6]

In our *Praxis of Statics*, in the Preface to the Reader, we have stated that bodies in motion do not move with a rapidity

[6] I have compared the Dutch of Stevin (Anhang der Weeghconst in his *Wisconst. Ghedachtnissen*, Leyden, 1605, pp. 170-1), and the French (Appendice de la Statique, Chapitre II, in *Les Œuvres Mathématiques de Simon Stevin de Bruges* ... Le tout reveu, corrigé et augmenté par Albert Girard, Leyden, 1634, 2.501.

related to the resistance they encounter, a statement the proof of which we have reserved for this point so as to refute the argument of those who think otherwise. First of all, Aristotle, with his adherents, thinks (see *Physics*, Book 4, the chapter on the Void) that when two similar bodies of the same density fall in air, their rate of fall is in proportion to their relative weights, that is to say, is relative to the interference they meet. And that such is his view he quite clearly shows in various places, as Book 6 of the *Physics*,[1] Books 1, 2, 3, and 4 of *De Caelo*, and in many other passages. This view has been attacked by Jean Taisnier, of Hainault, who concedes the existence of a proportion in so far as he maintains that the said bodies pass through equal intervals in equal times; an opinion shared by Cardan, *De Proportionibus*, Book 5, Proposition 110. That both men go astray we shall prove by actual experiment, and then make clear the reason. But the experiment against Aristotle is like this: Take two balls of lead (as the eminent man Jean Grotius, a diligent investigator of Nature, and I formerly did in experiment) one ball ten times the other in weight; and let them go together from a height of 30 feet down to a plank below—or some other solid body from which the sound will come back distinctly; you will clearly perceive that the lighter will fall on the plank, not ten times more slowly, but so equally with the other that the sound of the two in striking will seem to come back as one single report. And the same thing happens with bodies of equal magnitude, but differing in weight as ten to one. Wherefore the alleged proportion of Aristotle is foreign to the

[1] That is a mistake; Book 6 of the *Physics* should not be cited by Stevin on this point.

truth. But another experiment, against Taisnier, is like this:
Take a fine, delicate thread of cotton or wool, and a packet of
the same material, to the weight of a pound, compacted till it
is dense and firm, and in shape like the thread; let the two go
together from a height of five or six feet, and you will see that
the thread lingers far, far longer in the air than the packet,
though the material of the thread is much more compact and
dense than the packet, which admits a great deal of air.
Wherefore an equal space is not traversed by the two with
like rapidity.

(20) GALILEO (1564-1642) [Treatise] *De Motu* [about
1590], Caput. . . . in quo demonstratur, diversa mobilia in
eodem medio mota aliam servare proportionem ab ea, quae
illis ab Aristotele est tributa. In *Le Opere di Galileo
Galilei, Edizione Nazionale* 1.262-3

Ut igitur ea quae sunt pertractanda facilius absolvantur,
considerandum est, primum, diversitatem inter duo mobilia
dupliciter posse contingere: vel enim sunt eiusdem speciei, ut,
verbigratia, ambo plumbea aut ferrea; different autem in
mole: vel sunt diversae speciei, ut ferreum unum, ligneum
alterum; differunt autem inter se aut mole et gravitate, aut
gravitate et non mole, aut mole et non gravitate. De illis
mobilibus quae sunt eiusdem speciei dixit Aristoteles, illud
velocius moveri quod maius est: et hoc in 4 Caeli t.26 [= *De
Caelo* 4.4.311ª19-21], ubi scripsit, quamlibet magnitudinem
ignis sursum ferri, et velocius quae maior esset; et sic
quamlibet terrae magnitudinem deorsum moveri, et, similiter,
velocius quae maior esset. Et idem, 3 Caeli t.26 [= 3.2.301ª26

ff.], inquit: Sit mobile grave in quo *b*, et feratur per lineam
ce, quae dividatur in puncto *d*; si itaque mobile *b*
dividatur secundum proportionem qua dividitur
linea *ce* in puncto *d*, manifestum est, in quo tempore
totum fertur per totam lineam *ce*, in eodem partem
moveri per lineam *cd*. Ex quo apertissime constat,
velle Aristotelem mobilia eiusdem generis inter se
eam servare in velocitate motus proportionem, quam
habent ipsae mobilium magnitudines: et apertissime
hoc dicit 4 Caeli t.16 [= 4.2.309^{b}13-14], dicens
magnum aurum citius ferri quam paucum. [The
editors of Galileo here note: 'Da "et apertissime"
a "paucum" è apposto marginalmente. Inoltre, dopo "magnitudines" Galileo aveva proseguito (e poi cancellò) come appresso: "et, hac eadem demonstratione repetita in sequenti
textu, subdit haec verba: Velocitas minoris se se habet ad eam
quae est maioris ut".'] Quae quidem opinio quam sit ridicu-
losa, luce clarius patet: quis enim unquam credet, si exempli
gratia, ab orbe lunae duae sphaerae plumbeae demitterentur,
quarum altera centies altera maior esset, quod, si maior in una
hora ad terram usque deveniret, minor centum horarum
spacium in motu suo consumeret? aut, si ex alta turri duos
lapides, quorum alter altero sit duplus in mole, eodem momento proiciantur, quod minore existente in dimidia turre,
maior iam terram sit assecutus? Aut, rursus, si ex profundo
maris eodem tempore ascendere incipiant maxima trabes et
parvum ex eadem trabe frustrum, ita ut trabes centies maior
sit ipso ligno, quis unquam dixerit, trabem centies velocius ad
summum usque aquae ascensuram esse? [From 'Aut, rursus,'
to 'ascensurum' was added by Galileo in the margin.]

[Treatise] *De Motu* [about 1590], Chapter. . . . in which it is shown that diverse moving bodies in motion in the same medium maintain a proportion other than the one which is attributed to them by Aristotle.

Now, in order more easily to solve the problem under consideration, we must first bear in mind that a difference between two moving bodies can occur in two ways: the bodies may be of the same sort, as, for example, both of lead or of iron, and differ in size; or they may be of different sorts, one, for example, of iron while the other is of wood, and differ either in size and weight, or in weight and not size, or in size and not weight. Of those moving bodies which are of the same sort, Aristotle said that the larger moves more swiftly, namely in *De Caelo* 4.26 [$= 4.4.311^a19\text{-}21$], where he writes that a given magnitude of fire is carried upwards, and the more swiftly as it is greater, and similarly that a given magnitude of earth is carried downwards, and, similarly, the more swiftly as it is greater. And again he says in *De Caelo* 3.26 [$= 3.2.301^a26$ ff.]: 'Let there be a heavy body, *b*, moving in something, and let it be carried through the line *ce*, which is divided at the point *d*; if, then, the moving body *b* is divided according to the proportion in which the line *ce* is divided at the point *d*, then clearly in the time in which the whole is carried through the whole line *ce*, the part will be moved through the line *cd*.' Whence it most clearly appears that Aristotle will have it that moving bodies of the same kind severally maintain the same proportion in their velocities that their magnitudes have to each other. And clearly he says this in *De Caelo* 4.26 [$= 4.2.309^b13\text{-}14$], where he says that a

large body of gold is carried faster than a small one. [The editors of Galileo here note: 'The passage from "And most clearly" to "a small one" is put in the margin. Further, after "magnitudes" Galileo proceeded with (and then canceled) the addition: "and having repeated the same demonstration in the text following, he"—Aristotle—"subjoins these words: 'The velocity of the smaller is to that of the greater as'." ']
How ridiculous is this opinion of Aristotle is clearer than light. Who ever would believe, for example, that if two spheres of lead were let go from the orb of the moon, one a hundred times greater than the other, and the greater reached the earth in an hour, the less would take a hundred hours in its motion? Or if two stones were flung at the same moment from a high tower, one stone twice the size of the other, who would believe that when the smaller was half-way down the larger had already reached the ground? Or, again, if from the depth of the sea there began to ascend at the same moment a very great timber and a small piece of the same, such that the timber was a hundred times greater than the bit of wood, who ever would say that the timber would ascend to the top of the water one hundred times more quickly? [The last example, from 'Or again,' was added by Galileo in the margin.]

(21) GALILEO [Treatise] *De Motu*; from the same chapter as the preceding extract, *Ed. Naz.* 1.273

Ut, verbigratia, si fuerint duo mobilia, mole quidem aequalia, gravitate vero diversa, et sit huius quidem gravitas 12, illius vero 8, at quaeramus proportionem inter celeritatem illius, cuius gravitas 12, in aqua descendentis, et celeritatem illius, cuius gravitas 8, in aëre descendentis; videatur, primo, quanto 12 velocius descendat in aqua quam 8, deinde videatur quanto citius 8 fertur in aëre quam in aqua; et habebimus intentum; aut, e contra, videatur quanto 12 citius in aëre descendat quam 8, deinde 12 quanto tardius feratur in aqua quam in aëre.

Hae, igitur, universales sunt regulae proportionum motuum mobilium, sive eiusdem sive non eiusdem speciei, in eodem vel in diversis mediis, sursum aut deorsum motorum. Sed animadvertendum est, quod magna hic oritur difficultas: quod proportiones istae, ab eo qui periculum fecerit, non observari comperientur. Si enim duo diversa mobilia accipiet, quae tales habeant conditiones ut alterum altero duplo citius feratur, et ex turri deinde demittat, non certe velocius, duplo citius, terram pertinget: quin etiam, si observetur, id quod levius est, in principio motus praeibit gravius et velocius erit. Quae quidem diversitates et, quodammodo, prodigia unde accidant (per accidens enim haec sunt), non est hic locus inquirendi: praevidenda enim nonnulla sunt, quae nondum inspecta fuere. Videndum enim prius est, cur motus naturalis tardior sit in principio.

[Treatise] *De Motu*; from the same chapter as No. 20, above; *Ed. Naz.* 1.273

For example, suppose two moving bodies equal in size, but differing in weight, and let the weight of *a* be 12, and that of *b* be 8; and let us seek the proportion between the speed of *a* weighing 12 descending in water and that of *b* weighing

8 descending in air. We should see, first, how much faster 12 descends in water than 8, and then how much faster 8 descends in air than in water; and we shall have what we sought; or contrariwise we should see how much faster 12 is carried in air than 8, and then how much slower 12 is carried in water than in air.

Accordingly, these are the universal rules of the proportions for moving bodies whether of the same sort or not the same, in the same media or diverse media, whether up or down.

But we must bear in mind that a great difficulty here arises, namely, that the said proportions are found not to be observed by one who makes the experiment. Thus, if he takes two moving objects of different sorts, which have such conditions that the one is carried twice as fast as the other, and then lets them go from a tower, certainly the swifter will not reach the earth twice as rapidly; rather, if it be observed, the lighter will in the beginning of its motion outstrip the heavier and swifter. What the diversities are, and in what fashion and whence these unnatural accidents occur (for they are 'per accidens'), this is not the place to inquire; for first of all we must see why the natural motion is slower in the beginning.

(22) GALILEO [Treatise] *De Motu.* Caput. . . . in quo contra Aristotelem probatur, si motus naturalis in infinitum extendi posset, eum non in infinitum fieri velociorem.

Ed. Naz. 1.329

. . . Primo, enim, si quid non admodum grave ex alto veniens aspiciemus, qualis esset vel lanae globus vel pinna vel quid tale, videbimus tardius quidem in principio moveri, sed tamen, paulo post, motum uniformem observare. Cur autem id in minus gravibus manifestius appareat, ratio est quia, cum incipiunt moveri, eo quod tantum virtutis contrariae habeant quanta est propria gravitas, sintque ipsa modicum gravia, modica, ergo, etiam erit virtus impressa contraria, quare et citius absumetur; qua absumpta, motu uniformi movebuntur: et cum tarde etiam moveantur, facilius erit talis motus uniformitatem observare quam in his quae citissime descendunt. In rebus autem gravioribus, cum multa in eorum descensu absumenda sit virtus contraria, maius etiam tempus ad eam absumendam requiretur; in quo tempore, cum cito ferantur, per magnum spatium descendent; quae magna spatia cum apud nos haberi non possint, unde gravia demittantur, non mirum est si lapis, ex sola turris altitudine demissus, usque ad terram accelerari videbitur; hoc enim breve spacium breveque tempus motus non sufficit ad totam virtutem contrariam deperdendam.

[Treatise] *De Motu.* Chapter. . . . in which, contrary to Aristotle, it is shown that if the natural motion could be extended to infinity it would not become infinitely swifter.

. . . For first, if we observe something not specially heavy coming down from on high, such as a ball of wool or a feather or the like, we shall see that it does indeed move more slowly at first, but a little after maintains a uniform motion. The reason why this appears more clearly in less heavy things is that, when they begin to be moved, they have as much of a contrary force as is their proper weight, and if they are but moderately heavy, then but moderate will be the contrary force in them, and this force will be quite quickly taken away; and when it is taken away, they will be moved with a uniform motion. And since they are moved more slowly, it will be easier to observe the uniformity of their motion than it is with those things that descend very fast. But in the case of heavier things, since the contrary force in them, that must be taken away in their descent, is very great, a greater portion of time is required to take it away; in which time, since they are carried very swiftly, they will descend through a great space; now since we cannot have at our disposal the said great spaces from which heavy bodies should be let fall, it is no wonder if a stone let fall merely from the height of a tower will seem to accelerate all the way to the ground; for this brief space and brief time will not suffice for the loss of all the contrary force.

(23) GALILEO [Treatise] *De Motu.* Caput. . . . in quo causa assignatur, cur minus gravia in principio sui motus naturalis velocius moveantur quam graviora.

Ed. Naz. 1.334

. . . Si multum aëris, quod in ligno est, illud velocius facit, ergo semper velocius, dum fuerit in aëre, movebitur. Experientia tamen contrarium ostendit: verum enim est, lignum in principio sui motus ocius ferri plumbo; attamen paulo post adeo acceleratur motus plumbi, ut lignum post se relinquat, et, si ex alta turri demittantur, per magnum spatium praecedat: et de hoc saepe periculum feci. Firmiorem igitur causam ex firmioribus hypothesibus ut hauriamus, tentandum est.

Oh, quam facile ex veris principiis verae extrahuntur demonstrationes!

[For the translation, see above, pp. 54-5.]

(24) GALILEO, [Dialogue] *De Motu* [about 1590]
Ed. Naz. 1.406-7

AL[EXANDER]. Quod hoc multorum opinioni adversetur, nil mea refert, dummodo rationi et experientiae congruat, et licet experientia contrarium potius interdum ostendat. Si enim ab alta turri lapis descendat, illius celeritas semper augeri videtur: hoc tamen accidit quia lapis, respectu medii per quod fertur, nempe aëris, est gravissimus; et cum discedat cum tanta virtute impressa, quanta est sua gravitas, discedit profecto cum multa virtute impressa, ad quam absumendam non sufficit motus ex altitudine turris: ex quo fit, ut per spatium unius turris semper intendatur celeritas. Quod si acciperemus aliquod grave, cuius gravitas non tam longe aëris gravitatem superaret, tunc profecto oculis ipsis cerneremus, ipsum, paulo post principium motus, semper uniformiter moveri, existente tamen aëre tranquillissimo. Et idem etiam in lapide accidere perspiceremus, si et ex locis altissimis demitteretur, et ita essemus constituti, ut semper eadem sub ratione lineam motus perspiceremus. Nanque etiam noster situs impedit, quominus

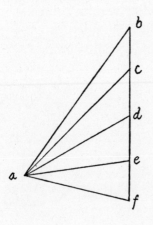

motus uniformitaten depraehendamus. Fiat enim motus uniformis ex *b* in *f*, et sint *bc*, *cd*, *de*, *ef* spatia aequalia; oculus autem aspicientis sit in *a*, et ducantur lineae visuales *ab*, *ac*, *ad*, *ae*, *af*: et quia motus ponitur uniformis, et sunt *bc*, *cd*, *de*, *ef* spatia aequalia, transibit ergo mobile per ea in temporibus aequalibus. Tempus ergo transitus ex *b* in *c* erit aequale tempori transitus ex *c* in *d*: motus tamen ex *c*

in *d* velocior inspicienti apparebit, cum et spacium *cd* maius appareat spacio *bc* (sub maiori nanque angulo spectatur). Et ita motus ex *d* in *e* velocior apparebit quam qui ex *c* in *d*, cum spacium *de* maius appareat quam *cd*, et aequali in tempore transeatur a mobili: et simili ratione, motus ex *e* in *f* velocior apparebit motu ex *d* in *e*. Quare et totus motus *bf* difformis apparebit, et semper in fine velocior, cum tamen uniformis supponatur. Oportet igitur ad diiudicandum motus uniformitatem et difformitatem, ut spacium sit adeo amplum ut in ipso possit mobile virtutem resistentem absumere, et ut oculus ita sit dispositus ut ab angulorum disparitate minime decipiatur.

[Dialogue] *De Motu* [about 1590]

ALESSANDRO. That this runs counter to the opinion of many does not concern me, nor yet that experiment sometimes may rather show the contrary. Thus if a stone descends from a high tower, its speed seems constantly to increase; but this happens because the stone with respect to the medium through which it is carried, namely air, is very heavy; and since it starts off possessed of a force of its own equal its weight; it starts off in fact with a great force, to get rid of which the motion from the height of the tower does not suffice. The result is that through the space represented by the single tower the speed is constantly increased. But if we take something having weight, yet the weight of which does not too far exceed the weight of the air, then indeed we perceive with our very eyes that the said object, a little after the beginning of its motion, is moved ever uniformly—supposing that the air is in a perfectly tranquil state. And we perceive the same thing happening with a stone if it is let go from very high points, and if we are stationed so as to see the line of motion, all of it, in one and the same ratio; for our position, too, interferes with our apprehending the uniformity of motion. Thus: let there be a uniform motion from *b* to *f*, and let the spaces *bc, cd, de, ef* be equal; but let the eye of the observer be at *a*, and let the visual lines be produced, *ab, ac, ad, ae, af*. Now, since the motion is assumed to be uniform, and as *bc, cd, de, ef* are equal spaces; therefore, the moving body will pass through them in equal times. Accordingly the time of transit from *b* to *c* will equal that from *c* to *d*; but the motion from *c* to *d* will appear more rapid to the observer, since the space *cd* looks greater than the space *bc* (for it is seen under [= is subtended by] a greater angle). And thus the motion from *d* to *e* will appear more rapid than that from *c* to *d*, since the space *de* looks greater than *cd* and is traversed in the same time by the moving body; and for like reason the motion from *e* to *f* will seem swifter than the motion from *d* to *e*. And hence the whole motion *bf* appears to be not uniform, though by hypothesis it is uniform. Accordingly, in order to judge of uniformity of motion and the lack of it, there must needs be an ample space, sufficient to let the moving body lose the resisting force in it, and the eye must be so situated that it will be least deceived by the disparity of the angles.

(25) GALILEO, *Discorsi e Dimostrazioni Matematiche intorno à Due Nuove Scienze Attenenti alla Mecanica e i Movimenti Locali.* ... Leyden, 1638. *Ed. Naz.* 8.108-9

SIMPLICIO. Ma chi posasse la maggior sopra la minore?
SALVIATI. Le accrescerebbe peso, quando il suo moto fusse più veloce: ma già si è concluso che quando la minore fusse

più tarda, ritarderebbe in parte la velocità della maggiore, tal che il lor composto si moverebbe men veloce, essendo maggiore dell' altra; che è contro al vostro assunto. Concludiamo per ciò, che i mobili grandi e i piccoli ancora, essendo della medesima gravità in spezie, si muovono con pari velocità.

SIMP. Il vostro discorso procede benissimo veramente: tuttavia mi par duro a credere che una lagrima di piombo si abbia a muover così veloce come una palla d' artiglieria.

SALV. Voi dovevi dire, un grano di rena come una macina da guado. Io non verrei, Sig. Simplicio, che voi faceste come molt' altri fanno, che, divertendo il discorso dal principale intento, vi attaccaste a un mio detto che mancasse dal vero quant' è un capello, e che sotto questo capello voleste nasconder un difetto d'un altro, grande quant' una gomona da nave. Aristotele dice: 'Una palla di ferro di cento libbre, cadendo dall' altezza di cento braccia, arriva in terra prima che una di una libbra sia scesa un sol braccio'; io dico ch' ell' arrivano nell'istesso tempo; voi trovate, nel farne l'esperienza, che la maggiore anticipa due dita la minore, cioè che quando la grande percuote in terra, l'altra ne è lontana due dita: ora vorreste dopo queste due dita appiattare le novantanove braccia d'Aristotele.

Galileo, *Dialogues and Demonstrations concerning Two New Sciences; Appertaining to Mechanics and Locomotion.* Leyden, 1638. *Ed. Naz.* 8. 108-9

SIMPLICIO. But what if one placed the larger stone upon the smaller?

SALVIATI. The weight would increase if the larger moved more rapidly. But we have already concluded that if the

smaller stone moved more slowly, it would in a measure
retard the speed of the larger, so that the combination would
move more slowly, though larger yet; and this is contrary
to your assumption. We thus infer that large and small bodies
alike, when they have the same specific gravity, move with
the same speed.

Simp. Your discussion is really admirable; yet I find it
hard to believe that a bird-shot is going to move with the
speed of a cannon-ball.

Salv. You ought to say a grain of sand and a millstone.
But, Simplicio, I trust you will not follow the example of
many others who divert the discussion from its main intent,
nor fasten on some statement of mine which wants a hair's-
breadth of the truth, and under this hair hide another man's
fault as big as a hawser. Aristotle says: 'An iron ball of one
hundred pounds, falling from a height of one hundred cubits,
reaches the ground before a onc-pound ball has fallen a
single cubit.' I say that they arrive at the same time. You
find, on making the experiment, that the larger precedes
the smaller by two finger-breadths; that is, when the large
one has struck the ground, the other is short of it by two
fingers. Now you would not conceal behind these two fingers
the ninety-nine cubits of Aristotle.

(26) VINCENZO RENIERI, *Letter* [*to Galileo in
Arcetri*]. Pisa, March 13, 1641. *Ed. Naz.* 18.305-6

Habbiamo qui havuto occasione di far un'esperienza di
due gravi cadenti da alto, di diversa materia, cioè uno di legno
et uno di piombo, ma dell'istessa grandezza; perchè un
tal Gesuita [Niccolò Cabeo] scrive che scendono nello stesso

tempo, e con pari velocità arrivano a terra, ed un tal Inglese affermava che il Liceti componeva qui un problema e ne rendeva la ragione. Ma finalmente habbiamo trovato il fatto in contrario, poichè dalla cima del campanile del Duomo tra la palla di piombo e quella di legno vi corrono tre braccia almeno di differenza. Si fecero anche esperienze di due palle di piombo, una della grandezza eguale a un'ordinaria d'artiglieria e l'altra da moschetto, e si vedeva tra la più grossa e la più piccola, dal' altezza dello stesso campanile, esservi un buon palmo di differenza, del quale la più grossa anticipava la più piccola. Quello che in tali esperienze mi venne notato è che m'accorsi che, acelerandosi il moto delle palle di legno fino ad un certo segno, cominciavano poi a non scendere a perpendicolo, ma per traverso, in quella stessa maniera che veggiamo che fanno le goccie d'acqua che cadono da' tetti, le quali, giunte vicino a terra, piegano per traverso, e quivi il moto loro cominciava ad esser meno veloce. Ho pensato a questo un poco, e ne dirò a V. S. Ecc.^{ma} il mio parere.

Se un mobile dovrà muoversi per un determinato mezzo, determinata ancora dovrà esser la velocità con cui lo potrà passare, in modo che chi volesse farlo andar più presto, il mezzo li resisterebbe, per non poter egli cosi presto ceder e dar luogo. Per essempio, io moverò con poca fatica una rosta, se la moverò con poco impeto; ma se la vorrò muover con grandissima forza, sentirò farmi resistenza dall'aria, e tal hora anco potrà impedirmene il moto. Dato questo, quando la palla di legno si parte dall'alto, movendosi con poca velocità e sempre più accrescendola, finalmente arriva a tal grado che l'aria potrà farli resistenza, e non potendo il grave più fender il mezzo a perpendicolo, penderà e piegherà da qualche parte, e poi fors'anco, ritornando a scender più velocemente, di nuovo anco tornerà a ritardarsi; in quella maniera che un foglio di carta va per aria hor a destra hor a sinistra piegando, prima che arrivi a scender in terra. Non so hora, se cadendo il piombo da una grandissima altezza, potesse arrivare a tal grado di velocità, che in lui si vedesse la stessa esperienza. Ci potrà un poco pensare V. S. Ecc.^{ma}, e in tanto compatirmi se forsi non mi sarò ben spiegato nella presente, che in fretta m'è convenuto scrivere per esser tornato tardi a casa.

[For the translation, see above, pp. 31-2.]

(27) VINCENZO RENIERI, *Letter* [*to Galileo in Arcetri*]. Pisa, March 20, 1641. *Ed. Naz.* 18.310

L'ultimo Dialogo di V. S. Ecc.^{ma} non è stato da me letto se non in qua e in là, perchè l'estate passata, che haverei potuto attendervi con diligenza, ella sa com'io stetti, e di poi non ho havuto tempo di poterlo vedere con quella applicazione che ricercano le dimostrazioni che sono in esso. So che è verissimo che due gravi differenti in specie, benchè eguali di mole, non servano proportione alcuna di gravità nello scendere, anzi che, per essempio, nell'acqua il legno si moverà al contrario del piombo; e però fin da principio mi risi della esperienza del Gesuita, che affermava che il piombo *et frustulum panis* (per dir com' egli scrive) si moveano con egual velocità al centro: ma che due gravi ineguali di peso, ma della stessa materia, cadendo dall'istessa altezza a perpendicolo, habbiano ad arrivar con diversa velocità et in diverso tempo al centro, mi pareva d'haver da lei udito o letto, chè ben non mi ricordo, non poter essere. Leggerò per tanto questi pochi giorni di vacanza l'ultimo suo Dialogo, benchè la total lettura me la riserbi a far questa futura estate con più commodo: in tanto torneremo a far l'esperienza delle palle, e vedere se ci fossimo ingannati la prima volta nella osservatione che quando s'avvicinano a terra pieghino e non vadino a perpendicolo, e ne darò avviso a V. S. E.^{ma}.

[For the translation, see above, pp. 32-3.]

(28) VINCENZIO VIVIANI, *Racconto Istorico della Vita del Sig.^r Galileo Galilei,* written 1654, first printed in 1717. The passage is taken from *Ed. Naz.* 19.606.

In questo tempo, parendogli d'apprendere ch'all'investigazione delli effetti naturali necessariamente si richiedesse una vera cognizione della natura del moto, stante quel filosofico e vulgato assioma *Ignorato motu ignoratur natura,* tutto si diede alla contemplazione di quello: et allora, con gran sconcerto di tutti i filosofi, furono da esso convinte di falsità, per mezzo d'esperienze e con salde dimostrazioni e discorsi, moltissime conclusioni dell' istesso Aristotele intorno alla materia del moto, sin a quel tempo state tenute per chiarissime et indubitabili; come, tra l'altre, che le velocità de'mobili dell'istessa materia, disegualmente gravi, movendosi per un istesso mezzo, non conservano altrimenti la proporzione delle gravità loro, assegnatagli da Aristotele, anzi che si muovon tutti con pari velocità, dimostrando ciò con replicate esperienze, fatte dall'altezza del Campanile di Pisa con l'intervento delli altri lettori e filosofi e di tutta la scolaresca; e che nè meno le velocità di un istesso mobile per diversi mezzi ritengono la proporzion reciproca delle resistenze o densità de'medesimi mezzi, inferendolo da manifestissimi assurdi ch'in conseguenza ne seguirebbero contro al senso medesimo.

Sostenne perciò questa cattedra con tanta fama e reputazione appresso gl' intendenti di mente ben affetta e sincera, che molti filosofastri suoi emuli, fomentati da invidia, se gli eccitarono contro.

[For the translation, see above, pp. 26-7.]

(29) WILLIAM WHEWELL, *History of the Inductive Sciences from the Earliest to the Present Time*. New York, 1859, 1.335-6

Aristotle's doctrine, that a body ten times as heavy as another will fall ten times as fast, is another instance of the confusion of Statical and Dynamical Forces: the Force of the greater body while at rest is ten times as great as that of the other; but the Force as measured by the *velocity* produced is equal in the two cases. The two bodies would fall downwards with the same rapidity, except so far as they are affected by accidental causes. The merit of proving this by experiment, and thus refuting the Aristotelian dogma, is usually ascribed to Galileo, who made his experiment from the famous leaning tower of Pisa, about 1590. But others about the same time had not overlooked so obvious a fact.—F. Piccolomini in his *Liber Scientiae de Natura*, published at Padua in 1597, says: 'On the subject of the motion of heavy and light bodies, Aristotle has put forth various opinions which are contrary to sense and experience, and has delivered rules concerning the proportion of quickness and slowness which are palpably false; for a stone twice as great does not move twice as fast.' And Stevinus, in the Appendix to his *Statics*, describes his having made the experiment, and speaks with great correctness of the apparent deviations from the rule, arising from the resistance of the air. Indeed, the result followed by very obvious reasoning; for ten bricks in contact with each other, side by side, would obviously fall in the same time as one; and these might be conceived to form a body ten times as large as one of them. Accordingly, Benedetti, in 1585, reasons in this manner with regard to bodies of different size, though he retains Aristotle's error as to the different velocity of bodies of different density.

(30) HUGO DINGLER, *Das Experiment; sein Wesen und seine Geschichte*, Munich, 1928, p. 239

Wir wissen heute dass Oresme schon diejenigen mathematischen Gestalten völlig beherrschte, die bei dem Galileischen Fallgesetz in Betracht kommen, und dass der Spanier Dominicus Soto (1494-1560), Beichtvater Kaiser Karls V, schon aussprach, dass die Fallbewegung nach diesen mathematischen Gesetzen vor sich gehe. Was blieb da für Galilei noch übrig?

Nun, sehr viel. Er war es, der das neue Fallgesetz, das er seiner Einfachheit wegen akzeptierte, zum ersten Male wirklich in die Erscheinungen hineintrug, der aus ihm nach allen Seiten hin die Konsequenzen zog und zugleich deren Realisierung in der Realität durchzuführen suchte. Er gewann aus diesem Gesetz die Zusammensetzung der Bewegungen, das Trägheitsgesetz, das Pendelgesetz und noch viele andere wichtige Folgerungen. So heisst er mit Recht der eigentliche Vater des Gesetzes.

Emil Wohlwill hat eingehend nachgewiesen . . . dass die Erzählungen von dem experimentellen Verfahren des Galilei bei der Aufstellen der Fallgesetze auf Sage zurückgehen, die zum Teil sein Schüler Viviani durch seine romantische Art der Berichterstattung aufgebracht hat. Nicht nur, dass die angeblichen Versuche Galileis am schiefen Turm zu Pisa fast sicher nicht stattgefunden haben, haben vielmehr seine Gegner solche Versuche gemacht, und Giorgio Coresio berichtet ausdrücklich, dass er die Aristotelische Auffassung dabei bestätigt gefunden habe. Und Galilei selbst spricht in der einschlägigen Pisaner Handschrift *De Motu* so wenig von Experimenten, dass er vielmehr ausdrücklich vor der Überschätzung des Experimentes warnt. ['Sed ut semper rationibus magis quam exemplis utamur (quaerimus enim effectuum causas, quae ab experientia non traduntur).] Galilei führt allerdings auch hier gelegentlich Experimente an, aber zufällig um gerade Behauptungen zu begründen, von denen wir heute sagen müssen, dass sie falsch sind (z. B. dass am Anfang des Falls Holz schneller falle als Blei).

Hugo Dingler, *Experiment; its Nature and its History*,
Munich, 1928, p. 239

We know to-day that Oresmius[8] was in complete command of those mathematical forms which come into consideration in Galileo's law of motion, and that the Spaniard Dominicus Soto (1494-1560), confessor to the emperor Charles the Fifth, had already said that the motion of falling takes place

---

[8] Nicolaus Oresmius, born *c.* 1323, died as Bishop of Lisieux, 1382; see Dingler, p. 224.

in accordance with these mathematical laws. What, then, remained for Galileo to do?

Well, a very great deal. He it was who, having accepted the law of fall because of its simplicity, for the first time brought it into the phenomena, drew from it its consequences on every side, and at the same time sought their full realization in fact. From this law he obtained the composition of motions, the law of inertia, the law of the pendulum, and still other impressive results. Thus he is properly called the real father of the law.

Emil Wohlwill has in exhaustive fashion shown . . . that the accounts of Galileo's experimental procedure in establishing the law of fall go back to tales which Galileo's pupil Viviani partly started through his romantic way of reporting. Not only did the alleged experiments of Galileo at the leaning tower of Pisa almost certainly not occur; far rather was it his opponents who made such experiments, and Giorgio Coresio expressly reports that he thereby found the Aristotelian view established. And Galileo himself in the relevant Pisan manuscript *De Motu,* far from stressing experimentation, does, rather, expressly warn against an overestimation of experiment. ['But, as ever, we employ reason more than examples (for we seek the causes of effects, and they are not revealed by experiment).'] On occasion Galileo does, indeed, adduce experiments, but, as it happens, precisely to support contentions of which to-day we must say that they are false—for example, that wood at the beginning of its fall goes faster than lead.

INDEX